AFFIRMING
the DARKNESS

AFFIRMING
the DARKNESS
An Extended Conversation About Living With Prostate Cancer

Chuck & Martha Wheeler
with Gretchen Hirsch

Received 3/4/97 from
Karen Wheeler Smith

Beverly, Massachusetts

1 4 3

Library of Congress Cataloging in Publication Data.
Wheeler, Chuck, 1921-1994.
Affirming the darkness: an extended conversation about living with
prostate cancer / Chuck & Martha Wheeler with Gretchen Hirsch.
p. cm.
Includes index.
1. Wheeler, Chuck, 1921-1994–Health. 2. Wheeler, Martha, 1923– .
3. Prostate–Cancer–Patients–United States–Biography.
4. Prostate–Cancer–Patients–United States–Family relationships.
I. Wheeler, Martha, 1923– . II. Hirsch, Gretchen. III. Title.
[DNLM: 1. Wheeler, Chuck, 1921-1994. 2. Prostatic Neoplasms–
personal narratives. WJ 752 W562a 1996]
RC280.P7W48 1996
362.1'9699463'0092 dc20
[B]

ISBN 1-889833-00-2

CONTENTS

FOREWORD

FOR VIRTUALLY HIS ENTIRE ADULT LIFE, Chuck Wheeler kept a journal. "God created paper and pencil so we could write things
down," he said. The result was a remarkable collection of com-
mentaries on his life and the world through which he moved.
When he was diagnosed with prostate cancer, the journal became
more than a collection of random observations. Recognizing that
his struggle with cancer was the defining and final activity of his
life, he closed the journal and began a new collection recording
his trip to the end of the line. He began these writings with a line
from Cornelius Ryan's *The Final Battle*, "Cancer follows me everywhere like a stray dog one hopes will just go away." Chuck's final
installment became known as "A Stray Dog."

This was by no means a solitary journey, however, nor is this
volume a solitary journal. For fifty years Martha Wheeler was
Chuck Wheeler's friend, lover, and wife. During the same period
she kept a companion diary of her own. These journals were not
only individual therapy—what he referred to as "working it out on
paper"—but also a means of honest communication. Each journal
was written in isolation and then, as appropriate, read by the other
partner. The edited combination of these two collections is a love
story, a medical primer about prostate cancer, and the story of a
journey of faith. It is the record of two expressive people *Affirming
the Darkness*.

There was a simple elegance in Dad and Mom's relationship.
The card-shop poster they chose to frame and hang in their bedroom said it all—a line drawing of a small boy and girl holding
hands, with the caption "I love being us together." While they
each had individual personalities, intersts, and friends, the domi-
nant force in each of their lives was their partnership.

They met in college and married precipitously, aided by the
reality of Chuck's impending service in World War II. When the
war was over they returned to their home town of Columbus,

Ohio, where, after another interruption by the army for the Korean War, they built the prototypical suburban life—two kids, two cars, a dog, and a house down the street from the high school. Chuck was an agent for New York Life Insurance Company, in addition to being deeply involved in community charitable activities. Martha was a wife and mother, first and foremost, and as we kids grew older, permitting her more independence, she also became a leader in community activities.

Open communication was the hallmark of the Wheeler household. Dad and Mom shared what was appropriate with us, but more importantly they shared with each other without reservation. This book reflects that openness.

This book is also a manifestation of "being us together." The intensity of their love never diminished: Chuck would begin each morning with a bouquet of kisses numbering the same as the date of the month; he called every day at noon; they had weekly dates and sent each other love notes. After we were grown, they started a new joint career and moved to Boston as "two for the price of one" development officers at a small college.

The promise of "being us together" into the future changed in 1986, when Chuck was diagnosed with prostate cancer. For the next eight years he and Martha confronted the physical end of fifty years of growing together. True to form, they did it as a team and with great openness. "I can even venture the opinion that cancer, if one must have it, is a gift," Chuck wrote. "It slows us down enough to be contemplative and to value life's most precious aspects, to know and to love each other more deeply and in ways probably known only by those who are vulnerable and threatened."

In their original form, these journals are much lengthier. Thanks to the editing of Gretchen Hirsch they have been condensed without losing any of their spontaneity or message. To aid the reader in differentiating between the two journals, Martha's writing is indented and in slightly smaller type. The names of some of the individuals have been changed in order to respect their privacy.

In this book, two remarkable people share with the rest of us a candid, sometimes wrenching personal journey to grace and God's love. Chuck was right: his cancer was a gift.

Tom Wheeler, Washington, D.C.
Karen Wheeler Smith, Sudbury, Massachusetts
July 1996

AFFIRMING
the DARKNESS

1
Chuck's Path
(1986–1989)

Sisters Ruth + husband Ray
Jack Taylor - urologist - Ohio
Stan G. O Chief of urology
Terry meadows - priest

In 1981, Chuck Wheeler's physician discovered an abnormality in his prostate. He underwent a biopsy, and no cancer was found. Until 1986, he was examined every six months. All test results were negative.

In 1986 Chuck and his wife, Martha, learned that he had cancer. Over the next three years they were caught up in the early phase of the disease, dealing with surgeries and recoveries, and coping with changes in their public, private, and sexual lives. It was a time of start and stop, crisis and resolution. There were long periods of relative peace punctuated by physician visits, tests, and learning about treatment options. At that point, they were still in a "cure" mentality, not yet understanding the road ahead.

*This section, although it includes a few of Martha's comments, deals primarily with the clinical issues surrounding Chuck's early struggles. He shares frankly and in detail subjects many men are reluctant to think about, let alone discuss. Both men and women will find useful medical and psychological information in these initial pages. In particular, readers will learn about the physical and emotion reactions that may accompany a prostatectomy, a penile implant, and an orchiectomy. ***

APRIL 8, 1986

Martha and I are visiting my sister Ruth and her husband Ray in Florida. Just before noon, I went to the bathroom, and holy mackerel, I urinated fresh blood and lots of it. I must have looked like a ghost when I returned to the kitchen.

I called Jack Taylor, my urologist in Columbus. He reassured me that it probably wasn't related to my prostate and that I should see him when I returned. He did suggest I might get a urologist in Florida to check me out for a potential infection and perhaps begin on an antibiotic.

---

* Medical terms related to prostate cancer and its treatment are defined in the glossary beginning on page 199.

As luck would have it, Ruth and Ray have both seen a urologist in Ocala. He said he would see me—and we were there in no time. A humorous man, lots of fun, he examined me and became very serious. "I don't like the feel of your prostate," he said. "You say a 1981 biopsy was benign, but if I were you, I'd go home and tell your urologist I said if you were my patient, I'd put you in the hospital and do another biopsy, post haste."

APRIL 21, 1986

Saw Jack Taylor today. It surprised me he didn't do his usual finger job, but said we should proceed immediately to biopsy.

MAY 9, 1986 *

The biopsy was done today, as well as a cytoscopy. Jack is confident all is well. He sees no change but can't explain the bleeding. He indicated there was a small growth, which he removed, on my bladder, but he seemed unconcerned about it. All in all we feel pretty confident that everything is OK and that we may never get a satisfactory explanation of the bleeding.

> I was on pins and needles to talk to Jack after the surgery and was relieved to discover he had found no change in the size, shape, or character of Chuck's prostate. I'm not the least worried about the lab report. In fact, I've talked to my cousin, who is a physician, and he feels if Chuck has gone five years from his original biopsy with no change and Jack saw none today, the growth is probably still benign.

MAY 15, 1986

It hit us like a ton of bricks—flattened us: I have cancer!

We walked to Jack's office under our umbrellas in a gentle rain. Relying on Jack's optimistic prediction, we bounced into the office and distributed sour balls to the girls. I noted they seemed more subdued than usual. Did they know something I didn't? I dismissed this improbability from my mind as I was escorted to Jack's office. He seemed subdued, too, but we exchanged raunchy jokes as usual. Then he got serious.

"Chuck," he said, "I've got good news and bad news. The

---

* Martha's journal entries, like the second entry for May 9, are set in a smaller typeface, indented left and right, and aligned with the date.

bad news is that we've found a few cancer cells. The good news is they're very low-grade."

"Wait a minute, Jack," I said. "Let's get Martha." I asked his nurse to bring Martha from the waiting room. "Martha, we've got problems," I said, as she sat down after what she describes as a long, long walk, knowing that her having been called in meant bad news. She looked fearful and vulnerable. "Tell Martha what you told me, Jack," I suggested, and he did.

It all gets rather foggy after that. We talked about his recommendation of surgery. Jack no longer does prostatectomies, but he wanted me to see Stan D., chief of urology at the Ohio State University Medical Center. We talked about the procedure, how I'd be opened up abdominally for laboratory examination of my lymph nodes, and how, if the nodes weren't cancerous, my prostate would be removed. If my lymph nodes were involved, I would be sewn up and treated otherwise. We talked about pre- and postsurgical matters and finally rose to leave.

Jack couldn't have been more compassionate. I can't remember when I've ever seen a doctor cry or seem as distressed as he was. The three of us stood there together and held one another, and as I looked outside at the pelting rain, I said, "The whole world is crying."

We walked the two miles home, oblivious to the rain. Life had caved in on us. I'm not sure what we said to one another.

The rain served only to wash away our tears.

How does one feel when her husband, lover, and buddy has been diagnosed with cancer? My heart fell to my stomach, my mind didn't want to accept it, my tears flowed at the slightest provocation. I seemed to be like a robot, putting one foot in front of the other, and yet I felt strength surge through me—such contradictory feelings! Each morning or in the middle of the night, the first thing I thought was, "Chuck has cancer." The thing to do now is have the surgery and hope the cancer can all be taken out.

JUNE 3, 1986

Tomorrow I'll be admitted to University Hospital for surgery. Gosh, I hope there is no involvement of my lymph nodes. I just want to be separated from the tumor.

So much has happened the past two weeks; various blood tests and x-rays; a bone scan and an MRI seeking tumors elsewhere in my body; a visit with Stan D., who agreed with Jack's diagnosis and recommended treatment. When Stan said, "Surgery will give you a good shot at fifteen years," that sounded fine to us. Martha's response was, "I'll take it, I'll take it."

Stan is a great guy. He takes time to explain; he includes Martha and relates sensitively to her, which is reassuring to me. He talks candidly about the surgical risks, about the inevitable incontinence that will follow (and that generally subsides and disappears within a few months), and about the temporary or sometimes permanent impotence.

> Stan sat us both down and talked straight about the surgery. He told us it would take about forty-five minutes to discover if the lymph nodes as well as the prostate were involved. If so, he would close the incision and Chuck would have radiation. If only the prostate were affected, the surgery to remove it would take three to four hours. I told him I didn't want to see him for at least three hours. When he asked when we wanted the surgery, I said, "Yesterday." He understood our eagerness to get it done and arranged the surgery for June 5. I'll never forget how he walked us out to the waiting room. With his arm around me, he said he'd do the best he could.

My presurgical fears are running high, one of the principal ones being a fear that some simple matter like a cold will cause the operation to be postponed. I've been taking tons of vitamin C to prevent that. Who knows if it has any effect? I've been sleeping fairly well, but often spend extended periods in the middle of the night when sleep eludes me. I recall the catchy tune the Wheelock College Glee Club used to sing, "Things That Go Bump In the Night." They do. At night, in the darkness, things seem much worse—overwhelming. I listen to the radio. That helps.

I am so impatient for tomorrow. Karen will arrive then to be with Martha for a couple of days, and then Tom comes for a couple more. Bless their hearts, they are so caring, so loyal, so supportive. They always have been. No one has been more blessed by their children than we have been.

JUNE 10, 1986

I came home from University Hospital yesterday. Gosh, they sure push patients out in a hurry these days—all part of Medicare's cost-containment policies.

It was a rough experience not only on me but also on Martha and the kids. The surgery went without a hitch, and when I awakened, I was delighted to learn that my prostate had been removed. That meant no lymph-node problems. Later I learned there was no apparent involvement of my bladder, seminal vesicles, or any tissue surrounding the prostate. All this was good and hopeful news.

A radical prostatectomy must be a bloody procedure. I was given three pints of blood. I recall the recovery room period to be difficult and painful.

Karen came the day before surgery, and what a tower of strength she was! It was hard for her because she's so close to her dad, and I'm afraid I wasn't much help to her, although I tried. She and I arrived at the hospital before surgery, and we walked beside his cart as far as the elevator. We went to the cafeteria for rolls and tea. Neither one of us was hungry, but we knew we should eat something. The cafeteria was so cold and unfriendly, hardly a supportive environment for two uptight women. We'd been told to go to the atrium during surgery and that Dr. D. would find us there after it was all over. We found a secluded place we could talk and still watch for the doctor.

When the first hour was up, Karen and I knew the first hurdle was over. Surgery began at 8:30 a.m. I was called to the phone about noon; the message from the surgical nurse was that everything was over, all had gone well, and Dr. D. would be down to talk to us in fifteen minutes. Karen and I hugged one another and cried.

When Dr. D. came, he took lots of time explaining everything. I then called Tom and gave him the good news. When I returned from the phone, Terry Meadows, the priest from St. Mark's, where Chuck and I go to church, came into the waiting area. She went with Karen and me to the cafeteria, where Chuck's friend, Don Gepfert, came looking for us to give us moral support and love. Friends and family are important always, but especially at times like this.

Having been told Chuck would be in recovery for two-to-three hours, Karen and I returned to his room to await his arrival. Around 3:00 p.m., a nurse came into the room and said they wanted Karen and me in recovery. Seeing the startled look on my face, she assured me that everything was OK, but that Chuck's blood pressure was so low they couldn't send him back to the room, and he was calling for us. They thought Karen and I could comfort him and perhaps get his pressure up. He had been given no painkillers since surgery because of the blood pressure, so he was in a great deal of pain when we arrived. The pain came over him in waves, and we would just hold his hands and stroke his forehead and kiss his cheek. It was decided he should have another pint of blood, and after that his pressure came up. Karen and I realized how important having blood becomes when the nurse had to almost beg to get it for Chuck.

We stayed in recovery about an hour. I had to leave a couple of times, but Karen stayed the entire time. I have great difficulty seeing someone in pain, especially a loved one. When I felt myself getting light-headed, I just quietly left. I didn't think the medics needed me complicating the situation.

On Monday afternoon, rather late in the day, Chuck and I learned that the lab reports said his cancer was a very virulent one. On the so-called Gleason scale of 1-10, his was a 9. We pressed Stan as to what that meant, and hesitatingly he said the probability was somewhere between 50 percent and 70 percent that Chuck would be alive in five years. He left the room, and I "hit the floor." Those were not the statistics I wanted to hear.

Shortly, Stan came back into the room, closed the door, and said he wanted us to know that even though the cancer was so virulent, there was no evidence of metastasis, and we should be "cautiously optimistic." Bless him for returning to talk more with us and giving us realistic cautious optimism.

I was nonetheless very upset, and we were grateful Terry Meadows came at that moment. Terry was a nurse before she became a priest, so she understands the statistics as well as the torment patients and families go through at such a moment. Terry was a great help; what a dear, loving, and caring person she is. As Chuck and I talked with her, I really began to see the whole picture and to realize how lucky we were that Chuck had had surgery, that there was no evidence of spread, and that we could deal realistically with both the positive side and the cautious side. I picked myself up off the floor, put my heart back in its place, felt strength from the good Lord, and was ready to walk into the future.

Whatever the situation, it's good to be home. My friend, the catheter, is still with me and will remain in place until three weeks after surgery, and would you believe it, Stan has sewn it to my penis—a stitch sewn into the glans with the thread tied to the catheter. Every time I move, it pulls; it's very painful. I'm going to talk with him about removing the stitch when I see him in a few days. What a great idea for torture!

JUNE 13, 1986

Stitches removed today. Stan was kind enough also to remove the troublesome stitch in the glans. I feel like a new man (well, partially). Next high point to anticipate is the removal of the catheter.

JUNE 30, 1986

My catheter was removed five days ago. It had felt like a tether—my constant companion. Good riddance! Now I am incontinent, an expected condition. I'm pleased, however, that I'm able to lie in bed without wetting. When I move from a sitting to a standing position, however, or when I walk about, there's no holding it back. I carry a wide-mouth jar with me when I'm walking around. I'm too sore to wear underwear or trousers yet, so pajama bottoms are the only alternative, and they give me easy access. Tubes still protrude from my abdomen and seep constantly, requiring frequent dressing changes.

JULY 23, 1986

Saw Stan today. In response to my complaint that my urine stream was too gentle, he did a cytoscopy and while up there cut away scar tissue at the point where my bladder connects to the urethra. I thought I'd go through the roof with pain. Stan kept saying, "Relax." Fat chance, even when he threatened to put me back into the hospital and do it under anesthesia. I didn't relax, just held on—and survived.

My incontinence is slowly improving, but I still wear a pad. When we walk, we have to plan our route to permit my going into a filling station, church, or school to change the pad. I bet the custodians in the buildings wonder how it is that they find wet pads in their trash baskets. But things are looking up. We flew to Detroit last week for a short visit and got along very well.

SEPTEMBER 13, 1986

The second tube finally came out of my abdomen, so I no longer need dressings. And the last external stitch came out of my incision. Hallelujah for both!

SEPTEMBER 30, 1986

No pads, no dribbles—an occasional accident, but I can live with that. Incontinence is humiliating, particularly at the onset when there was simply no ability to hold back my urine.

One day we ran into our friend Alice while we were walking. We asked how long her husband Hugh had been incontinent after his prostatectomy. She replied, "Oh, six to eight months." I nearly fell over. Perhaps my four months wasn't so bad. Some guys, they say, never regain their continence and have to undergo corrective surgery.

One night in July, though, I hit my absolute low. We were at a nice party at the Herbsts—perhaps twenty people for dinner and an evening on the patio. When we got up to leave, I realized I had overflowed my pad, and I was soaked, literally soaked, from my knees to my waist. Thank goodness the patio was dark, and I was able to get to the car and home without being noticed. I wondered what the chair I'd been sitting in looked like.

But now all that is behind me, and I'm ready to work on potency. I am totally impotent. Stan is hopeful he didn't damage my nerves during surgery, but he did say that, regrettably, he beat them up pretty badly. He wants me to wait a year before we make the decision on a penile prosthesis. Hugh, Alice's husband, once described his impotence as "all the wires being down." Most apt. Poor Martha.

> [Martha wrote at a later date about this period] Once Chuck was stronger, we began to travel extensively. Travel—going new places and seeing new things or visiting friends and relatives—is one of the things I love most to do. Prior to Chuck's illness, we had bought two Senior Passes, as TWA euphemistically refers to them. We called them Old Poops' Passes. and they were good for travel anywhere in the United States anytime. The only two restrictions were that we had to travel through St. Louis to our destination city, no matter where it was, and we were only allowed two trips to any one destination.
>
> Our first trip was from Columbus to Detroit—through St. Louis—just a few weeks after Chuck's surgery. He did well, and that encouraged us to continue on. Our next trip was Columbus to Boston—again through St. Louis!
>
> As Chuck regained his strength and thoughts of cancer receded,

we went into high gear, traveling fifty thousand miles in the next year–to Seattle, Los Angeles, Las Vegas, Tucson, and Hawaii; to Washington, D.C., to see Tom and his family; and back to Boston again, to visit Karen and her husband and boys. It was perfect; we were carefree, happy, and active. It was the last time.

NOVEMBER 29, 1986

We went to Hugh's funeral today. He waged a good fight against prostate cancer. He was originally diagnosed in 1974, but it finally got into his kidneys and bladder. He had a kidney removed and his bladder rebuilt. He had both chemotherapy and radiation. Now that's what I call battling.

DECEMBER 30, 1986

My impotence is a concern to me. My dear Martha is paying such a price. We have always been very active sexually, and now it is impossible. Did you ever try to stick a marshmallow in a piggy bank?

Many years ago, I told Martha that should I ever become impotent, I hoped she could and would find sexual pleasure elsewhere. That was naive. While I could understand why she might, it would not be in keeping with Martha's nature and temperament. So while she patiently waits, we try in every conceivable way to satisfy her. We're getting pretty good at it, but it's no substitute for real sex.

I "beat my tool" to death urging it into an erection, and Martha tries too, but all to no avail.

> [Martha wrote at a later date] We felt so bereft without our intimate life that Chuck endured injections of a drug directly into the penis. The resulting erection was supposed to last several hours–a good deal longer than needed. After the first shot, we drove home giggling and smirking like two teenagers preparing to hop into the back seat of a Buick. We stopped quickly at the grocery to pick up a quart of milk, and as we walked through the aisles, Chuck said, "You know, honey, people are going to wonder about that look on your face." But he was grinning, too. We had to wait in line a minute, and by the time we reached the outer doors of the grocery, the drug had worn off. All that expectancy for nothing! Chuck tried the injections again, but they just didn't work for him.

> On one of our last trips on the Old Poops' Passes, we headed off

to Puerto Rico. We stayed in a convent that had been turned into a hotel, and it was such a lovely, romantic atmosphere. Our last evening there, after a delicious dinner accompanied by wonderful music, we were very much in the mood to enjoy one another physically. We tried everything imaginable, but there was no way it was going to happen. Chuck was crushed, and so was I.

He was champing at the bit to try a prosthesis. I wanted him desperately, but I was leery about another surgery. "You don't have to go through that," I said. "It's really not that important." But the more we talked about it, the more we saw that, for us, it was that important, so off to surgery Chuck went again.

FEBRUARY 25, 1987

Still impotent, but Stan is now willing to install what Martha and I refer to as a peter pump. Stan has shown us three types and has set a surgery date of April 28. This whole exercise will cost about $10,000. It will take a lot of sex to amortize that cost, but we're ready to try.

APRIL 27, 1987

Prosthesis surgery.

MAY 10, 1987

Good grief. Nobody told me. I couldn't believe the pain. If people ask me if I recommend a prosthesis, my answer will be, "It depends on how important sex is to you. If it's important, it's worth it."

[Added later] Other doctors have since said that the pain Chuck experienced is not typical of this type of surgery, and that there must have been other reasons for his discomfort. They were unable, however, to tell us what those reasons might be.

MAY 16, 1987

We are at the Inn at Honey Run with our Couple's Circle. I'm still pretty uncomfortable—still have to "wear" my penis up my belly—but things are a lot better than they were a year ago when we announced my cancer to this same group in this same place. I'm not very good company up here, carrying my pillow into the dining room, and staying in my room while others go here and there, but I'm here, and that's a victory.

We had lunch yesterday with our good friends George and Barbara. He has prostate cancer with metastasis to the lymph nodes. Orchiectomy was the only treatment available. He is about six months postoperative and has had a very difficult time, both physically and emotionally.

MAY 27, 1987

Cancer has struck another dear friend. Bill learned of his disease about a week ago and came to see me. He cried in my arms like a child. But it is another case of early detection and aggressive treatment. On my recommendation, he is being treated by my urologist.

JUNE 6, 1987

Yesterday, on the first anniversary of my prostatectomy and a few days more than a year since our last intercourse, Martha and I made love. What joy! What an experience! In response to my query, "Will I come?" my doctor had said, "You'll think you do." I kidded Martha that I felt like the little engine that could: "I think I can, I think I can." And later I said, "I think I did, I think I did, I think I did."

We're going to have to learn how to operate this new prosthesis. In its flaccid state, my penis is enormous, far too much for the limited confines of my jockey shorts and trousers. In an erection, it is too easily broken; I lose it as I use it. But it is sure better by any measurement than it has been for the last year. We've only made love once since getting the peter pump, but I'd undergo all the pain and discomfort a dozen times again for this.

Jeanne G. has been a good friend to Martha. She knew about the prosthesis because her husband had also had one. She, being sensitive to Martha's needs and sexual starvation and also being one who speaks openly and freely, counseled Martha before my recent surgery. When she invited us for cocktails after, she said, "You've used it." We compared notes and it was reassuring and helpful. She said to Martha, "The best part is that you don't have to sleep in a pool of it any longer."

It's interesting that I haven't previously made notes regarding Jeanne's husband. He died of prostate cancer just a few days before my surgery. I must have blocked that out.

In spite of the fact that the character of an erection is different when it isn't spontaneous, our first lovemaking was wonderful. It was glorious to fully express our love again, to be intimate in the way that was so meaningful for us.

SEPTEMBER 11, 1987

My former urologist Jack Taylor's funeral was today. Cancer got him, a malignancy of the esophagus. He must have had it when he told me about mine, although I doubt he knew it at the time. He was apparently diagnosed about a year ago. It seems as if the whole world is getting cancer.

MARCH 2, 1988

We've been cruising along for quite a while feeling better and better about everything. Two years ago, after surgery and after the lab work was complete, my doctor, when pressed, gave me a 50-to-70 percent chance of surviving five years. We had interpreted that to mean that if I survived five years, he would consider me "cured." With two years behind us, we were beginning to feel increasingly confident. Cautious optimism had nearly given way to confidence.

I made reference to this today on a visit to Stan. He brought me up short, saying that there was the potential for metastasis for as long as fifteen years, and he went on to say that if another year passed without a metastasis, he thought we could add a year or two to the first five in his original odds. That brought us back to reality with a thud. Tonight we are regrouping in the context of the new reality. But our optimism continues.

APRIL 17, 1988

Two more friends have been operated on for prostate cancer. The other day I made a list of friends and acquaintances who have had it—eighteen men, fourteen within the past couple of years. Four more are already dead.

JUNE 5, 1988

The second anniversary of surgery and the first year since the resumption of our sexual activity. It was so fitting that University Hospital chose today to celebrate Cancer Survivors Day. Invitations were sent to five thousand known survivors of cancer to attend a celebration on the plaza in front of the hospital. Several hundred survivors and spouses showed up. They served punch and cookies; we heard a few upbeat remarks; and at the end, we released balloons into the air, each balloon bearing a small tag showing one of our names.

It was a *good day*. Survivors talked to one another openly and easily—something that is hard to do in society. And often we were surprised to spot an acquaintance we had not previously known was a cancer patient. It was amazing to me that more survivors didn't come, just to celebrate by putting their bodies in the plaza, but we were grateful for those who did attend. I hope such an event will be held every year, and that Martha and I will go to many of them.

JUNE 6, 1988

I flunked my PSA [Prostate Specific Antigen test]! This is not good. It means the cancer has metastasized. But Stan said it could be an anomaly and we'd repeat the test in thirty days. My PSA has been cruising along at about 2.4, but is now at 4.5, the upper limit of normal being 4.3.

Back in March, when Stan corrected our understanding of the odds for survival, he told us that while my PSA had been consistently normal, if it should increase sharply and abruptly, we would begin "treatment" immediately. To me, that sounds like hormone treatment and radiation of the suspicious spot on my spine.

I'm afraid of hormone therapy. I've been told that female hormones have the potential of adverse side effects, such as weight gain and breast enlargement. That treatment has always been something to avoid. Perhaps when Stan says "treatment," he means orchiectomy—removal of the testes. We're back in limbo again, and limbo sucks.

JUNE 29, 1988

Quarterly blood test and annual bone scan were done today—always a source of some anxiety for both of us. We're a little jumpy today, however, because the folks in nuclear medicine took several additional enlargement scans of an area of my spine.

JUNE 30, 1988

Dr. D.'s nurse called and asked me to return to the hospital for some x-rays of my spine. I was there within the hour. Now I *am* jumpy.

JULY 1, 1988

Stan called about 4:30 to say he knew I'd want to know that the x-ray people said the suspicious spot on my spine is arthritis, and since it's a long weekend, he wanted us to have the good news today. We are indeed fortunate to be in his capable hands.

JULY 15, 1988

Martha went to see Bob M., her doctor, to adjust her arthritis medication. In the course of conversation, she brought him up to date on my PSA and bone scan. Bob said, "You know, Martha, there is no cure for Chuck's cancer, but results have been excellent in trying to slow it down."

That was a bummer. It was real, specific, and factual, but we know down deep that what he was saying was that the horse is out of the barn—that we are probably confronting metastasis. Stan hasn't used that word, but Bob, in his straightforward way, is telling it like it is. We are stunned.

JULY 22, 1988

We are in Boston, having driven up from a short visit with Tom and his wife, Carol, in D.C. and then an overnight visit with a friend in Montclair. We have dumped on the kids, given them the full story as we know it, and speculated about possibilities for the future. It isn't easy, but it is necessary. It is part of their maturing, and they must work it out for themselves.

The kids handled it well. Tom, the stoic, didn't say too much, but down deep it hurt. Karen, always the more emotional one, cried, but began to work it through with class. Our grandsons dealt with the news in their own way. Brian had only a modest response, internalizing it in his own always private manner. Colby, more like Karen, came apart.

As we were going to bed, Karen came in and asked me to go in to relate to Colby. He was on his bed crying. I lay down beside him—really couldn't say too much more than, "It's OK to be afraid." I held him in my arms, and we were just together.

August 3, 1988

I had my follow-up blood test last Friday. I flunked again. This time my PSA was 4.9. Stan made time for us, and as we sat in his office, he gave it to us straight, honestly, and sensitively. We are confronting a rapidly rising PSA and a suspicious spot on the spine. He said the nuclear-medicine experts had labeled the spot metastatic cancer, but the x-ray people had called it arthritis. Stan said he could live with the arthritis diagnosis until time could confirm it, but in the presence of the change in PSA, he was leery. He then said we had three alternatives:

• Do nothing at all. Watch and wait. He said he would support us if we chose this course of action.

• Radiate the spot on my back. This might be an inappropriate treatment inasmuch as there's a difference of opinion as to what the spot is. The only way we could ascertain with certainty if it's malignant would be to do a biopsy, and Stan is unwilling to recommend that. So radiation might be directed at the wrong spot if it really is arthritis.

• Perform an orchiectomy—removal of the testes and with them the source of hormones on which the prostate cancer thrives. He said fully half of informed urologists would not recommend this treatment now, but he is in the half who would.

I said, "Stan, let me ask you. Am I correct in saying the original surgery in 1986 was a shot at a cure, and that we had a good chance of achieving it?" He said yes. Then I followed with the critical question. "Are we now dealing with a situation where cure is no longer in the cards? We're now moving to a 'slow it down' mentality?" Again he said yes.

Martha asked if the orchiectomy would reverse the increase in PSA. Stan answered, "We hope so." And to her question, "Will it cause the spot on the spine to disappear?" his answer was the same.

We talked about the side effects. He reassured us that an orchiectomy does not change the tone of a man's voice, as is commonly thought, but will inevitably result in impotence. As

I'm already impotent, this is of no concern to me, but for many men it is a significant deterrent to having the procedure. There is a potential for experiencing hot flashes, but if they become troublesome, there are medications to relieve them.

I looked at Martha and she at me, and I knew then that I was about to lose the family jewels. We were in total agreement about the choice.

Stan then told us that in doing the orchiectomy he was attempting to buy more "good days." He used an example of forty months, saying if I should live forty months, he would anticipate that twenty of them would be good months, far more than if he did not remove the testes. He talked about dying and said dying from this cancer is not particularly painful. I was grateful for the comment.

But I must confess I was reading between the lines. While he didn't and wouldn't make any specific prediction in my particular case (although he did say with an orchiectomy one might expect a fifty-fifty chance of five-year survival), I wonder why he chose the example of forty months and why he chose today, at this moment, to inform us of how death finally comes.

AUGUST 11, 1988

I had the orchiectomy yesterday, and it was pretty much a breeze—outpatient surgery under a local anesthetic (albeit with heavy sedation). I was operated on at 10:45 a.m., out of recovery at 12:30, and home by mid-afternoon. Unbelievable!

There will be one great benefit to all this. As I grew older, my testicles had become a source of discomfort to me, hanging so long they sometimes dangled in the toilet water. In addition, my testes had been somewhat painful since the prostatectomy, and I had always had great difficulty getting down into a tub of hot water, they being so sensitive to the heat. Not any more, and Stan even took a "tuck" in the scrotum to make it smaller.

I'm pleased with the minimal mutilation this has caused. I guess I suspected I would lose a lot of scrotum. Not so. While there is far less mass of tissue than before, there is enough to identify, and I have more room in my underwear and trousers for my enlarged penis now that there are no testes. No loss without some small gain.

Apparently some men have an emotional depression after

this procedure. I find no hint of such and don't expect it. Seems to me I can get along without my balls at age sixty-seven, although I'm a bit anxious about how this will effect our sexual activity. I hope I don't lose any more of the sensation of orgasm. I've already lost too much.

AUGUST 17, 1988

Martha and I had a rather intense exchange today around the word *metastasis*. While I confess I'm not sure, Martha heard Stan refer to the spot on my spine as "possible metastatic carcinoma." I heard only "metastatic carcinoma."

What is clear is that both of us have avoided the use of the word *metastasis*. But I used it today, to Martha's great distress. We worked it through and now acknowledge that we would not have proceeded to the orchiectomy unless the doctors had been confident metastasis had occurred.

Ah, words.

AUGUST 22, 1988

Hallelujah! Stan called today and said my PSA was 2.6, back down within normal limits. That's the first good news in two and a half years. In addition, the pathology report on my testes was negative. So in only six days, the orchiectomy is having the desired effect. My cancer is being slowed. My elation is enormous, but I'm also stunned. I didn't realized how reconciled I had become to the continual barrage of bad news. One would think I'd be dancing a jig, but I find myself quietly contemplative. I had conditioned myself to a much less favorable report.

Rationally I know how fortunate we are; emotionally I find it hard to believe or accept. I feel like I've been standing on the gallows with a noose around my neck, awaiting the drop of the trap door. Now it's as if someone has said, "Here, friend, let me loosen that rope, and why don't you just go on back to your room."

We know what this means and what it doesn't mean. All Stan offered was that I'd have more good days. We willingly accepted it. And now it seems this gift is a reality, and for it we are grateful beyond words to express.

AUGUST 20, 1988

Martha talked with Alice today, and this was of tremendous help to her. We need to talk with others who have walked a similar path, because conversation with those who haven't is often downright unhelpful.

AUGUST 27, 1988

Today I changed the registration of our bank deposits and our mutual funds to joint tenancy with right of survivorship. It was not an easy thing to do, and I have been resisting it. Although the necessary forms had been on my desk for nearly a month, I had not brought myself to deal with them. Martha and I had for so long owned all our assets individually, a form of ownership compatible with the trust settlement of our estates. But recently we concluded that none of the former reasons for having trusts remains, and so we terminated them and returned to simple wills, bequeathing all our assets to one another. Having done that, it makes little sense for us not to own our assets jointly, and it will save several thousand dollars of probate expenses in my estate.

Actually changing the registration was difficult for more symbolic reasons. It was an act of preparation for dying, and it hit me hard. It was another way of recognizing reality. Not that my death is imminent. Far from it, but I do know that the odds favor its occurring sooner rather than later.

It's nothing new in the course of human history, of course, but it's sure a new concept for me.

SEPTEMBER 8, 1988

I'm pissed off. That's what I told Martha last evening in a fit of anger. She wisely responded, "Well, thank goodness you've said it. It's OK to be angry." And then she described my previous attitude as one of having been grateful for all that has been done to me. Of course I'm grateful. Who wouldn't be grateful for early detection and aggressive attack?

But I'm also pissed off. I'm angry that I have cancer at all, and that the disease is so intrusive. I'm angry about all the physical damage that has been done to my body. I'm angry at the loss of my prostate and its vital orgasmic function; the change of my penis into an organ that is really too large for my comfort; the loss of my testes and the newly acquired hot flashes; the loss of my sexuality and my potency; and the reduction of intensity of both my desire and my functioning.

Now, these are a small price to pay for life and good days, and I would willingly undergo it all again. But it does make me angry that all of this has assaulted the very heart of my manhood.

SEPTEMBER 16, 1988

We have returned from the best trip we've ever experienced. We flew to Seattle, where we leased a car and drove for nine days and seventeen hundred miles through the Canadian Rockies. Returning to Seattle, we spent three nights with our good friends Marj and Ron.

Something magic happened to us on this trip. Martha calls it a spiritual experience. It really was. Perhaps it was the ambiance—magnificent mountain scenery of breathtaking beauty. Perhaps it was the fact that we were away alone, just relating to one another. Perhaps it was the leisurely pace, starting late and stopping early, or the reading and writing we did, the latter crystallizing so much of the sense of vulnerability and assault that has pervaded our lives these recent weeks. I don't know what it was, but it was sheer delight and fed our souls.

I have thought a lot during the past couple of years about the question of cancer treatment. How much would I be willing to accept and of what sort? The idea of chemotherapy has been unattractive to me, perhaps because a physician friend once said to me, "Once you start on chemo, you can never expect to have another good day." I have observed chemotherapy patients, and I have not been encouraged. The toxicity seems overwhelming, the cure as bad as the malady, and it seems to me that it serves only to postpone the inevitable—to string out the stress for all concerned. I asked patients and their families if they would choose it again and got inconclusive, contradictory responses.

Had I been asked about it, I would have responded that one never knows what he will do under any given set of circumstances until he gets there, but deep down, my thought was that I probably would refuse chemotherapy. But something happened during our trip, and one day as I drove, I penned a note to myself: "Chemo OK." It just came over me that to decline any treatment, chemo included, would be to capitulate to cancer, and that I decided I would never do—never, that is, until it is clear that it would be futile and that there is little likelihood of buying any more good days.

All my days are good now, and I have had nearly 850 of them back-to-back since my surgery in 1986, and I really don't know what bad days are and can only imagine how they might be. But I have resolved now to keep fighting with every tool at hand as long as there are any good days and a reasonable expectation for more of them—or until the bad days become unbearable for my family or for me.

SEPTEMBER 17, 1988

In spite of the fact that our trip was less than a month after the orchiectomy, I am pleased with the stamina I mustered. We were careful not to go at a pace or do those things that would result in excessive fatigue. We were both pleased at the way I trudged up a long path at high altitude and often at a steep incline as we sought the extraordinary view of the glaciers on Mount Edith Cavelle. It was a good test.

But I do fatigue easily, and it seems to me that it is more than postoperative fatigue. Martha correctly points out that I have always needed an abundance of sleep and that I am even now only six weeks postoperative, but I know that fatigue is a factor in my life these days, and while it is, in and of itself, not terribly significant, the fact that weakness occurs is new. On some occasions the weakness in my legs is so pronounced it's difficult for me to make it up a normal flight of stairs.

The good news is that as long as I avoid fatigue, the weakness does not manifest itself.

SEPTEMBER 20, 1988

Conversation with another friend with cancer pointed up some real differences in coping styles. Bill is upbeat almost to the point of denial. He rejects my intense focus on cancer and feels I'm setting myself up with negative, self-fulfilling expectations of gloom and doom. He prefers to set up what he hopes are self-fulfilling expectations of a cure and tells himself that the more he can think of and expect cure, the more likely he is to obtain one.

Bill has a dear friend who writes books and conducts seminars on these matters, and Bill has great confidence in him. Bill is also a patient of Stan's and seems to be caught in a trap between Stan's recommendations and those of his friend. He seems somewhat skeptical of Stan and has even mentioned finding another urologist.

It seems to me positive thinking is very useful in producing a supportive *attitude* in a patient and his family. But to accept it as the route to a *cure* is, to my mind, excessive. I don't doubt for a moment the psychosomatic relationships of disease and healing, but I am far more willing to cast my lot with the Stan D.s of the world and combine that choice with a positive attitude on all our parts.

SEPTEMBER 23, 1988

How much do I tell Martha? How much do I record in these pages, knowing that she will read them and that I want her to do so? We're confronted with a values conflict. We have always been open with one another, but I am so reluctant to dump on her, to cause her any more stress than she would have simply in the natural course of events. Right now she has a full plate. Her mother continues to live when any hope of good days has long since disappeared; my cancer causes her to be super-alert to any signs of deterioration, and her apprehension is very real; her own arthritis is a continuing source of pain and discomfort; and she faces bravely our move to First Community Village, a retirement community, another act of positioning ourselves for the future. She really doesn't need any more.

Should I tell her that yesterday my urine was a darker color? Was it something I ate or drank—or a taint of blood? Or was it my imagination and anxiety? In ten days, I see Stan. But in the meantime, should I tell Martha?

We had a rather emotional exchange on this subject in the Seattle airport recently and continued it as we flew to Minneapolis. We worked it through and felt a lot better about it (talk is so therapeutic) but it caused us both considerable distress. Our conversation centered on how real I can be in this journal and still fulfill my need to protect Martha. She supported my desire to let it all hang out in these pages and expressed her conviction that she could handle it. As a matter of fact, given our customary openness with one another, she would feel somewhat threatened if I recorded less than everything or urged her to refrain from reading what I wrote. But she also understood my need to protect her.

While I think we came out on the side of openness and sharing, I think we also recognized that perhaps the price of this mutuality is a "*mostly* total revelation."

OCTOBER 4, 1988

Just came from another visit with Stan. What a great guy. So caring, so thoughtful, and so reassuring.

He was a bit defensive, I thought, when I referred to our choice of orchiectomy as "aggressive." He walked me through the alternatives, this time talking about various approaches he could have recommended, each of which had potential adverse side effects. But he eased off when I was able to finish my question and ask if the aggressiveness of the orchiectomy, when my PSA was only moderately over upper limits, was related to the virulence of my type of cancer.

His answer was an emphatic yes. He then went on to say that although a PSA could go up into the hundreds (I had heard of one at 250 or more), any PSA in the range of 8 to 12, or any marked increase over a brief period of time, as in my case, warranted immediate intervention. He puts great importance on the PSA, saying it is the only test that reveals prostate activity at an early date—twelve to sixteen months before any other indicator.

He said the orchiectomy offered great promise for more good days and months, and although there are no statistics to support any particular conclusion, he was hopeful the surgery would extend my longevity. It seemed to me, though, that he was more confident of the greater number of good days than of increased life span. He continues to point with enthusiasm to the two-plus years his father-in-law has had since his orchiectomy without further elevation of PSA or other symptoms.

He believes that my fatigue and the weakness in my legs are not associated with the disease but simply the result of the trauma of three surgeries in two and a half years. He is not surprised that my sexual desire has markedly diminished and I have not had an orgasm since the orchiectomy. He does not expect a return of these functions. I said that after the prostatectomy I was impotent, and after the orchiectomy I was really impotent. He responded ruefully, "Well, I guess you could put it that way." He anticipates that my hot flashes—a frequent occurrence since the orchiectomy—will subside. (Hallelujah! I feel like a menopausal male.) It was a good visit. He took time as never before. He has always been great at relating, but today was special. I feel confident and reassured.

I record all these things because I feel as if we are at the beginning of a new period of watchful waiting and of many good days made possible by the caring treatment of a skilled physician in whom I have unlimited confidence. What a blessing to have confidence in a world where so many human beings have so little and are so critical of others!

OCTOBER 25, 1988

We have never been so content, so happy, so excited about the future. It seems incongruous, that's for sure, but it's true. Something deep down in my gut tells me we will be blessed with lots of good days. Although not even the professionals can predict with any degree of accuracy, something inside me says we'll have two or three good years and then a couple of years of putting out fires, which will get us to five years and our fiftieth anniversary. From then on, it feels uncertain.

We are now in negotiation to move to First Community Village, there to set down our roots and make our home an environment of caring and support, no matter what comes. It feels right for us to do this while things are good and while we can enjoy it together. And it feels good that our kids will not have to be responsible for us, nor will they have to "put" us there when things begin to break down. For me, this commitment to move to the Village is a final act of planning and love for those I love most. There is nothing else on this earth I can do for them. Now I can only live out my days with enjoyment and excitement for each one, with the certain knowledge that Martha is secure and that the kids and their families are well on their way. Why wouldn't a guy be happy and excited for the future? This guy surely is! But even more, I am at peace.

NOVEMBER 1, 1988

Informed participation, it seems to me, is an important part of treatment, far more gratifying than what seems evident in the cases of nearly everyone else I know who is post-operative or post-radiation. Almost to a man, they seem uninformed—almost uninterested—in what has happened and is happening to them. They live in the euphoria that "everything is fine." Little as I know, I can hardly engage in conversation with them because they seem to know or understand so much less.

Perhaps my need to be informed is my way of coping; perhaps their manner is their way.

NOVEMBER 7, 1988

These days are *so good* it seems impossible that anything could be amiss, that anything could be wrong inside my body. It's as if I were in the beautiful, calm, sunbathed eye of a hurricane. I feel so good—spiritually, emotionally, and physically. I continue to ponder my happiness. It is not a screwed-on euphoria. It is a genuine happiness at the core, characterized by peace, contentment, and well-being.

Perhaps as time passes, I will think less and less about my cancer. The shock of metastasis this summer was profound and preoccupying. Perhaps it will be less and less a part of my conscious thought as more time separates me from the metastasis and the orchiectomy, as was the case following my original diagnosis and surgery. But my happiness is undeniable, and I am sure that, at least in part, that happiness comes from our focus on the joy of the good days.

Our emotions are very near the surface. Church services touch them off, as do great music, expressions of love from family and friends, and artfully chosen words.

From time to time, Martha gets on "overload," rather easily, I perceive. Those are difficult moments for me; I feel so helpless. But it is to be expected, I'm sure. Thanks be to God that she and I find it so easy to cry and are so permissive of one another's tears. Sometimes we cry together over seemingly modest matters, but while it reveals how close our emotions run to the surface, it washes away the hurt and releases tension. Time, talk, and tears—how many times we have commented about these great healers and how grateful we are that we permit each to happen!

NOVEMBER 29, 1988

My PSA is 1.3. Hallelujah! Guess I can get along without balls.

Holidays and family moments are special, filled with tender experiences (when they are permitted to happen, and we are frequently and customarily permissive in this respect). We have just returned from our typical Thanksgiving reunion with my sisters and their families—Pauly, Jim, Ruth, Ray, Mark, and Phil—in North Carolina. Prior to that, Karen, her hubby Doug, and their sons, Brian and Colby, were here for several days, during which fell our forty-fifth anniversary and Karen's fortieth birthday. So I am deeply involved with memories of family closeness and sharing.

While we were driving home from North Carolina, my mood settled into quiet contemplation of many things. As the miles ticked off and beautiful music filled the car, I thought a lot about dying. Some say it's morbid to think about dying. I disagree. It is real, probably more real than any other thought. What is more certain or more permanent or will involve a longer period of time? Can you imagine, if you had the capacity to think prior to your own birth, that you wouldn't think about it and the new life to come?

I wondered, as I traveled along, about saying goodbye to Martha and how I hope we have the opportunity. I thought about the extreme pain it will cause her, and I was fearful about that, and I wondered if there would be equivalent pain for me— or if the impending release and the excitement of moving into a new dimension would mitigate the pain. I wondered if it would be possible to say goodbye to beloved friends, to touch and perhaps embrace them as I thanked them for their friendship. Or would it be too difficult for them? Would it heap on unintended pain? Perhaps it depends on the person and the degree to which we have previously been able to talk about what matters most. I wondered about the appropriateness of participating in planning my funeral and burial. I have some strong ideas about this. It isn't necessary to discuss them now, but is it any of my business? Or is it the business of my survivors? After all, such occasions are for their benefit, in spite of survivors' propensity to speculate that "he would have wanted it this way."

Ella Fitzgerald was filling the car with classic favorites, often considered light, breezy, and expressive of happy relationships. But in my mood of reflection, the words had a stinging poignancy. (Martha later confessed to the same feeling.)

> There may be trouble ahead, but while there's
> moonlight and music and love and romance,
> let's face the music and dance. . . .

> How far would I travel to be where you are?
> How far is the journey from here to a star? . . .

> I'd love to rest my weary head on somebody's
> shoulder. I hate to grow older all by myself.

The words of these songs stung and burned, and I was overcome by a deep sense of helplessness and vulnerability.

DECEMBER 29, 1988

Our sex life has deteriorated to an uncharacteristic and disappointing level. My libido is nearly nonexistent. While my prosthesis stands ready to serve up an erection on demand, I have no desire (except an intellectual desire to satisfy Martha). I have no capacity for an orgasm or even to think I'm having one. While Martha and I continue to enjoy and need physical closeness, from me she gets no "vibes," and I don't feel I have any. It is as if I am a log lying beside her. We continue to try, but success is so limited we find less and less motivation. It is all terribly frustrating and disappointing. The loss of sex is a separation experience, another one of those experiences like death, divorce, a broken relationship. It is addressed only by grief. The waning of the sex drive that comes to all as times passes and as age progresses is far more easily accepted than the jolt of its sudden cessation.

All this has occurred since the orchiectomy. At first we thought that it was postsurgical trauma and that my libido would return, but it has not. I feel as if I am leaving Martha high and dry. I feel like a runner with no legs, a motor without sparkplugs, an engine without steam.

Because my prosthesis will permit it, I tell Martha I can give her all the sex she can handle, but she says it takes a two-way flow of current. Her feelings and concerns are valid. She fears that aggressiveness on her part will make me feel inadequate. She is concerned that my impotence will result in guilt because it thwarts her sexual needs. Because there's no "playback" from me, her libido suffers from lack of stimulation, and she worries that I feel diminished by her lowered desire. She wonders how I interpret it.

Impotence is a profound experience for those for whom sex has been an important part of the marital relationship and bonding, which for us grows each year of our married life. The inability to achieve an erection—corrected by the prosthesis—was one thing, but the loss of desire, mutual stimulation, and fulfillment is something far more significant. Stan says that it shouldn't be so and that we should read books to stimulate ourselves. We say we have read much through the years and have tried all sorts of techniques as we explored each other and our sexuality. Right now we are hoping for a restoration of our sexual capacity.

DECEMBER 31, 1988

Today I talked to my old friend George, who also has prostate cancer. His metastasized before it was discovered, so he had an orchiectomy and hormone treatment. Recently his PSA was elevated, his bone scan revealed more metastasis, and he is beginning to experience pain. George is one who has chosen to learn little about his condition or about the disease. He copes by ignoring—not denying, just ignoring. We haven't be able to relate very well about our common predicament, but his recent worsening has left him devastated.

Talking with him was a heavy experience. Among the fifteen or so people I know with this disease, he is the first one who has "broken down," the first one to go into what I consider Phase III. On the other hand, it was rewarding to see again how useful it is for me to be informed and aware, not only about my present situation but also about the possibilities and probabilities that await me.

I don't know whether being informed and participative heightens my feeling of vulnerability—perhaps it does—but I'm certain there is enormous value in dealing with reality on a daily basis. Untoward events can happen, and we'd better face the facts head-on today, tomorrow, and throughout the uncertain future. To do otherwise is to risk devastation at the very time when stability is needed most.

As a footnote, I need to comment on the importance of a spouse who shares and can handle this way of coping. I can only imagine the confusion and conflict that would arise between spouses whose methods of coping differed markedly. Martha's and mine differed initially, but the realities of the past three years have brought us closer, not only in our relationship with one another, but also in the way each of us copes. I honestly feel that we support and are helpful to each other as we walk this trail together.

2
Walking Together
(1989–1992)

After Chuck's cancer escaped (metastasized), he and Martha began to understand that there was a sniper in the house, a sniper that for weeks and months was silent, only to squeeze off another round when it was least expected. They began to accommodate the day-to-day realities of this slowly encroaching intruder and became more anxious and worried. As they lost friends to prostate cancer, they were disheartened by the progression of Chuck's disease. They fretted about pain, change, separation, and death. But because they were an unusually communicative couple, they were able to talk out their stresses and come to the conscious decision that they would enter into the process of living and dying, while "affirming the darkness" that occasionally enclosed them—to "make something good out of it for ourselves and others." They continued to enjoy their family and to serve their church and community. They traveled, they entertained, they lived in the present, and they began to explore more deeply issues surrounding life and death and their beliefs about the afterlife.

It was during these years that the couple discovered that Martha, too, was ill. A brain tumor, although benign, required delicate surgery and a protracted convalescence, which added additional tension to an already difficult period.

Yet faith abounded, and this section offers an in-depth look at that faith and how it sustained the Wheelers as they faced the dailiness of living with cancer and the crisis of Martha's unexpected illness. Although they never denied the facts of their lives, they maintained their sense of peace and thankfulness for the positive people and situations they encountered. Resisting anger, resentment, bitterness, and "why me?" they celebrated each moment, even as they planned carefully for their inevitable separation.

JANUARY 10, 1989

My PSA is 1.7! The hormone approach continues to be successful.

FEBRUARY 2, 1989

In all of this, Martha and I have committed ourselves to doing those things that will help others who share this predicament understand and tolerate their own circumstances better. Last evening we had an opportunity to do that in an unusual way. Riverside Hospital sponsors a weekly television program, with audience participation, on various health issues. The program was on impotence, and we were members of the panel. The audience, perhaps fifty in number, were a mixed group of old and young, curious and silent. The questions to me concerned the experience of impotence and having a prosthesis implanted. To Martha the questions centered more on being the wife of an impotent spouse, her feelings, and her observations of my response.

We felt as if we had made a bold presentation and that we had imparted information that could be helpful to a listener. But we also felt exposed, as if we had voluntarily revealed much that to many would be so private. Those whom we have told about our participation have been aghast, and I guess we understand because they've never been impotent and can't imagine being so, let alone talking about it on TV. We feel good and wholesome about it. Having been through so much together, I guess we take as commonplace much of the experience, and thus feel little inhibition about it.

MARCH 2, 1989

Chemotherapy has been suggested for George, but he has refused it. Instead he's launched himself into the unknown, the unapproved, the peripheral treatment. He has placed himself and his future in the hands of an M.D. who professes to fortify the immune system through intravenous injections and diet. The treatment is not reimbursable through insurance or Medicare, and the doctor requires all the money up front in some sort of trust fund. For me, it fails the sniff test, but George has anecdotal evidence to point to the success of this physician's approach.

George also feels God gave him cancer, thereby singling him out as "special." He feels that perhaps God wants him to participate in this new treatment and that therefore it is incumbent on him to submit. It seems to me he is flying in the face of all the time and effort expended by the best minds in the world, which makes me very uncomfortable.

All this once again raises the issue of chemotherapy. I know there is no cure for my cancer when it has metastasized, and that chemo is designed to slow it down and extend life—but at what price? It seems to me there are two kinds of prices to be paid. First there is the price the patient pays in terms of discomfort and side effects. But second, and equally important to me, is the price paid by the family. In my case, what would it do to Martha as she watched and waited? What would the treatment do to Karen and Tom? Would it be helpful to them in dealing with my disease and its inevitable result? Would it give them peace and hope, or prolong their agony? Does this treatment consti- tute heroics? Does it add quality of life or only duration?

It's evident I have no answers, only questions. I also could be accused of borrowing trouble. I could ignore the questions today and postpone dealing with them until the issue of chemo becomes a reality. But this is such a potentially important deci- sion, I'd rather be prepared to make a clear, level-headed deci- sion and not to be forced into something by the crush of cir- cumstances. If and when the time comes to consider chemotherapy, I want to make an informed choice built on a firm philosophical base—a base on which I can stand with some degree of comfort and acceptance.

It was good to have this experience with George. It moved the whole issue out of the abstract and revealed the magnitude of the decision George has made, a decision that may one day come to me as well.

MARCH 15, 1989

We are anxious, and we know it. We are anxious about the uncertain future. Now that Martha's mother is gone—and with her death our anxieties for her—our attention has shifted to my cancer. It seems as if our anxieties are most pronounced before each quarterly visit to Stan and the inevitable blood tests. My next visit is in three weeks, and we are also coming to the time of year when I have my annual bone scan. Last year, it was these tests that revealed the first indication of metastasis, which resulted in my orchiectomy.

Our anxieties get expressed in different ways. For Martha the fact that we have not yet sold our condo and thus cannot move to the Village is agonizing. I am equally anxious about selling and about getting a fair and reasonable price. In addition, I fret about the added expense of maintaining both our apartment at the Village and the condo, about the $100,000 of capital we have expended to establish ourselves at the Village, and about the heavy monthly expenses and the threat of constant increases as inflation continues to gnaw at the economy. And I think about the fact that until we move to the Village, we do not begin to work off the one-year waiting period for full medical coverage (assisted living or health-care-center support) at reduced rates. And I'd be less than honest if I didn't confess to anxieties about not surviving to enjoy our new and somewhat protected life together.

Recently, Karen invited Martha and me to come to Boston to be with Brian and Colby while she and Doug are away. Martha badly wanted to go. Rationally I did too, but emotionally I was so hesitant I simply couldn't bring myself to agree. I pointed out several practical considerations why we shouldn't go. On a couple of occasions, I actually agreed to go, but later reneged. I worked myself into a heightened emotional condition and felt just plain miserable about the whole thing. I felt guilty and yet at the same time simply unable to make this trip. When we finally decided not to go, I was greatly relieved. Even at the time, I knew I was experiencing a genuine anxiety attack, and I was unable to explain it then or now. I simply had to accept it. Better than to deny it, I said.

APRIL 5, 1989

Stan asked me about my libido, and I indicated that it's zero. He offered me a medication that is often effective with impotence; he thought it might help elevate my desire, and strange as it may seem, I demurred, saying I really didn't feel comfortable taking hormones. He assured me that this medication was not a hormone, but still I held back. Sensing my reluctance, he pulled back too and said he wasn't going to push me.

Rationally I am reluctant to take any more medication, particularly medication that's optional. It seems to me I'm already taking all I want to take on a regular basis, and who knows what kinds of chemicals will be going into my body as time passes? I did wonder, however, if the absence of my libido was contributory to my lack of desire for the new medication. Does one need desire for desire?

I told Stan that we were getting along OK and that Martha seems content with things as they are. But on the way home, I wondered if I was being fair to her, and I felt some guilt about not taking Stan's offer. Martha and I discussed it, and she reassured me by saying that she was satisfied both sexually and with my decision. I offered to get back to Stan and ask him to prescribe the medication, but Martha said she didn't think that was necessary, and then she commented about the proliferation of medication and about mixing this one with other medications.

Although I remain uncertain about this choice, I think we'll stick with it. Strange as it may seem, I think there are more important things in life than sex—or is my loss of libido showing?

APRIL 10, 1989

Bob asked Martha about my energy level; she told him it was somewhat lower than in the past. He assured her that this was to be expected, adding that our habit of walking four miles each day is very helpful. He urged us to continue to walk, saying that this activity would contribute to slowing the cancer.

I wouldn't be honest, however, if I failed to acknowledge my declining energy. Although I keep going, it is easier and easier to sit. After we return from our walk, I find it helpful to collect myself and restore my energy. It is increasingly difficult for me to get down on the floor and more difficult to get up again. My legs refuse to let me squat, and getting out of a chair requires some determination. Stairs constitute a barrier; hills wind me more. Perhaps this is nothing more than the toll of years, but it seems these changes are more rapid than I would have expected.

Falling has been more of a threat. I seem to trip and fall easily, and my balance, which has always been troublesome, is even less dependable. I observe these things and wonder. I have had twelve hundred good days back-to-back since my original surgery, but, in all honesty, these good days are not quite so good as they once were.

MAY 2, 1989

Martha and I are finding great satisfaction in ministering to others out of our experience, counseling those who are dealing with cancer, impotence, and the use of a penile prosthesis. We hope it is helpful for those we counsel; we know it nourishes our own souls. In these days of uncertainty, exciting as they are (and they are exciting), the need to feed our own souls is immense. I'm not quite sure what it means to feed one's soul, nor am I certain what one does specifically to derive such a feeling. I only feel a compelling need to minister, and I know the feeling of peace and assurance that comes over me when my soul is nourished.

Feeding one's soul has something to do with separating the important from the nonessential, identifying the real, acting on the meaningful, and focusing on God's gifts to us, not the least of which is life itself.

MAY 6, 1989

One of the most persistent issues Martha and I face is the question of how much it is desirable (or beneficial) to know and understand. Each of us has a different level of need in this respect. I need to know more than Martha, but Martha needs to know everything I know, so she ends up knowing more than she needs.

Intertwined in all this are the two roles—those of "watcher" and "watchee," as we like to put it. To me, the watcher has it far more difficult. The anxiety that cancer produces in those who stand by helplessly, the frustration in not being able to do anything about it, the fear of inevitable suffering, the specter of ultimate separation, the ease and quickness with which one's mind relates any minor symptom or change to the illness—all this must be terrible. While Martha is strong and tough, accepting and understanding, she is still human in every way, and I can feel her underlying concern and anxiety and her sense of foreboding.

For us the answer is, and always has been, to talk it through and share our feelings, which keeps the issues alive in our minds. We feel this is preferable to suppressing our thoughts, feelings, and concerns. I hurt for her. How I wish I could lighten her burden and carry her load, but I'm convinced that shielding her is of no value, and avoidance of all the feelings associated with this disease benefits no one.

MAY 10, 1989

Here we are still in our condo, while our beautiful new apartment is ready for us at First Community Village. When we put the condo on the market last November, we really thought we'd be living at the Village early in the year; we never thought we'd still own this place after six months. We've had forty-seven showings without one offer!

This has been a difficult time for both of us, as we're so eager to move and get settled and get on with life. It's not that we can't and aren't getting on with life as we stay here; it's that selling is our first priority and anything else comes after that. I naively thought that after Mother died and we got over that trauma, we would sell and be on our way—traveling to see our kids and grandkids, going to Florida, or just doing what we wanted to do when we wanted to do it.

I'll admit I want us to travel when Chuck is feeling fine and there are no problems. I don't expect problems, but I'm anxious because I'm acutely aware that someday the cancer will take over. I'm not pessimistic, only realistic. I don't think it will happen soon. In fact, I'm quite hopeful it will be many years, but that's not for me to know. Traveling is not what bothers me; it's feeling limited in what we can do when I want us to feel free.

I've been thinking a lot about my anxieties lately, and I understand I'm also grieving for my mother. The fact that Chuck's life is threatened makes me more susceptible to anxiety. Perhaps it's also that Tom Meadows, the husband of our dear friend and priest, Terry, was diagnosed with prostate cancer this week and is very bad, as the cancer is already in his bones. Tom's predicament has opened up the whole reality of how deadly this disease is. It shows me how vulnerable I am—we are—and that makes me anxious.

When we were in the Pacific Northwest last fall after Chuck's orchiectomy, we both got our heads screwed on straight again, and we really felt peaceful at the core; so it surprises me that I have this anxiety when I still feel peaceful. My inner peace must come from the fact that I recognize the anxiety and can talk and write about it.

Tom Meadows is number twenty-two on my list of friends with bladder or prostate cancer, and it appears his case was well advanced at the time it was discovered. When we were first

dealing with my cancer, it was Tom's wife, Terry, who minis-
tered to us again and again so significantly and so tenderly.
And now it is Tom and Terry's turn in the barrel and our turn
to minister to them, although it appears they are already far
worse off than we have ever been.

We identify with them so completely. For us it is a painful
re-enactment of so much, and it dredges up, all over again, the
agony of being introduced to the reality of having cancer. But
in spite of the pain, it feeds our souls to be able to relate to
them in a way that eases their burden and enables them to
accept and cope.

MAY 25, 1989

Tom Meadows continues to struggle. He is waiting for the beneficial effects of Flutamide, hoping it will slow down the cancer. The disease is too far advanced for surgery and the metastasis is too extensive for radiation. Perhaps the Flutamide will
be effective, but in the meanwhile his symptoms persist and
intensify.

And now comes word from George. Although he declares
his unconventional dietary approach effective, he is back at the
hospital. His prostate cancer has metastasized to his bladder,
and he is also running a bacterial infection. The bladder tumor
has closed off his left ureter, so now he is dealing with a new
condition.

These two friends have caused us great concern, first for
them, but second because their deterioration has given us a
glimpse of the manner in which this disease progresses. I would
be less than honest if I didn't admit to a feeling of foreboding.

From the outset both Tom and George presented far more
advanced cases than I did, and for me that is encouraging. We
are so grateful for early detection and aggressive treatment.

JULY 26, 1989

It has been limbo time again—that period when everything goes
on hold pending the results of examinations, tests, and deci-
sions regarding courses of action.

Today was the day for my quarterly blood test and my annual bone scan. We've been apprehensive for a couple of months.
I have been concerned as I experienced transitory discomfort in

my back, hips, and one elbow. I have written it off as arthritis, problems of aging, and even imagination, but there has been a lingering uncertainty.

I felt uncomfortable not revealing my discomfort and apprehension to Martha, but it seemed pointless to concern her when there were no real answers until the current scan and blood work were done. We have discussed these issues again, and I am sure there is no easy answer. While on one hand it can be argued that there was nothing to gain by revealing my nervousness, it is equally evident that Martha experienced my apprehension and felt separated from me when I was reluctant to talk or to answer her questions both about how I felt physically and about the upcoming tests.

So it was today that we journeyed over to University Hospital for the tests. While the results of the PSA have not yet been determined, and while it will be another full week before we see Stan for evaluation, it was revealed that my cancer is progressing—the metastasis is continuing. Bless his heart, the doctor in nuclear medicine called us back to his office to view the films of the bone scan, comparing last year's with today's. While the tumor on my spine was still as evident as before, it hadn't grown. However, two new tumors have appeared, one in the thoracic area of my spine and a second in a rib. It is interesting, though, that there appears to be no abnormality in the areas that have been giving me discomfort.

Martha is crushed again. She had been so hopeful, but wise enough and demolished often enough to know that her hope was only that—and was not based on any evidence. She knew she would have to wait for the facts. She's strong and courageous, but her pain brings me pain. My hardest problem is to watch and experience what my cancer does to her and the kids.

She asked me how I felt. Without having thought about it previously, I answered with the analogy of being caught in a fast-moving stream, being carried along by a current too strong to resist or escape and, right now, being tumbled head-over-heels and brushed by unseen rocks. I know that downstream there will be more rapids and tumultuous currents, but also some calm and placid waters, some overhanging branches to grasp, and some shallows where I'll be able to plant my feet firmly. I know there's a great waterfall over which I'll surely plunge. But I assured her that until the plunge becomes inevitable, I will fight the current, grasp the branches, stand in the shallows, and withstand the assaults of the hidden rocks. I'll give it one hell of a ride. That is my commitment to her, to the kids, to myself, and to life.

AUGUST 1, 1989

Chuck and I have talked a lot about affirmation—affirming the cancer, accepting it. We don't like it one bit, we wish it weren't there, but it is there, and denying it won't help. In addition, I've learned to affirm and accept my own anxiety. I have accepted the fact that I am anxious and that it is OK. It is a natural feeling, and in accepting it, I find that it doesn't rule me.

When anxiety rules, it is hard to live each day to its fullest and to enjoy and to be grateful. In accepting Chuck's illness and my anxiety, I'm affirming the wholeness of life, as life holds both goodness and sadness. In affirming and accepting, I find it easier to stay in touch with God. When I am in denial or filled with anxiety, I can't "hear" God; I make it too difficult for myself. When I accept, I find I am more in tune with God and feel His support and love. The thought of Chuck's suffering is difficult for me, but since suffering of all kinds is part of life, I trust that Chuck and I will both be sustained with the strength that comes from God. It has always been there, so I trust it will continue to be.

While walking this morning, Martha and I talked some more about affirmation—the things one must feel, think, and do to affirm, because we have concluded it is paramount for both of us to affirm this travail. Although we may discover more about affirming as time passes, it now it seems to us it involves:

- Acceptance. We must accept my cancer, Martha's potential widowhood, our probable pain, the pain and stress my disease brings to the kids, and their need to resolve these matters in their own ways with their own spouses. To accept is to recognize and face the fact that all these things are a part of life—not a welcome part, surely, not one to be sought after or rejoiced about—but nonetheless a part of the process of living.
- A recognition that life is not picking on us. Nothing is happening to us that hasn't happened many, many times before

to millions of others; it is simply a new experience for us. We are not being singled out. We are just caught up in one of life's difficult experiences.

- An acknowledgment that suffering is OK. Through all of life we try to avoid suffering for ourselves and for those we love. Inevitably, however, there will be those moments and experiences in which physical, emotional, and mental suffering is unavoidable. Surely suffering should not be sought, but it is a part of life.

- A renewed opportunity to hone the fine edge of one's ability to trust God. We always walk into the future by taking one more step into the murky, uncertain areas that lie before us, and we do it with trust in the unseen forces so evident around us. In the depths of our individual and collective unconscious are indescribable forces of guidance, support, and wisdom that bubble up into our conscious awareness. Are these God? I think so.

One also needs to trust the professionals—not to be perfect or flawless, but to give their best shot. One needs to take one's hands off the wheel (not exactly easy for me) and let the others drive.

August 4, 1989

My PSA is 1.8, holding firm. Stan says the orchiectomy is doing what it's supposed to be doing—slowing down the cancer. We had been prepared for much worse news and for a recommendation for new treatment, but it didn't come. We had focused our attention on the two new metastatic sites without knowledge of the PSA—another illustration of jumping to conclusions with inadequate facts.

It has happened before that after receiving good news, I have been stunned and found it hard to deal with. Martha's mood soars up like a yo-yo. Mine remains on the floor temporarily, until I can appreciate the news—until I can get my thoughts and emotions lined up. Martha and I discussed the fact that our diverse responses put a temporary stress on our relationship. It is clear that these quarterly visits, and the emotional build-up to them, are a source of considerable anxiety for both of us. We see it in ourselves and in each other; we allow for it. We each try, with all our capacity, to be respectful and understanding of the other's apprehension. It isn't always easy, but I think we do it well. We sure as hell give it a go.

I am fearful of Martha's upswings because I'm fearful of the fall. My initial mood is to protect her. While Martha is increasingly realistic in her responses, she still jerks herself up on the yo-yo string. She's normally a positive, upbeat, optimistic person, often without supporting evidence, and when she gets some supporting evidence, she releases her positive characteristics in reaction. My style is to gather the facts, look at them head on, shake the hell out of them, and proceed with caution, protecting myself, I'm sure, from a potential fall or disappointment, just as I try to protect Martha.

There is another more shadowy aspect to my response. As a child, when confronted with a plate of food, some of which I liked and some of which I didn't, I would always eat the food I didn't like first, getting it behind me and saving the good stuff until last. I've always lived my life that way, doing the disagreeable first, getting it out of the way. A piece of me feels that way about my cancer. Let's get on with this disagreeable experience. If it must be, then let it be. But, as Martha says, this isn't like going overseas (another disagreeable event we longed to get behind us), because from cancer there is no coming home again.

This feeling of wanting to get on with it makes me uncomfortable. It smacks of a death wish—and perhaps might be if it weren't a lifelong style—but I know I don't want to die. I know I don't want to suffer the personal pain of the disease or the emotional pain of watching Martha and the family agonize. I don't want any of this, not that first whit, but to some degree I find myself caught in this crazy contradiction between being grateful for every good day and the deep-seated desire to get on with it.

In spite of all these contradictions, I'm happy for this apparent reprieve.

AUGUST 10, 1989

This week, we've been absorbing a lot of straight stuff. We got it from Stan as he evaluated my progress and painted some pictures of my probable future. He mentioned steroids and chemo as possible treatments, so I called the National Cancer Institute

(NCI), and they sent me some material. It turned out to be an overview of prostate cancer and the suitability of various treatments in various stages. The material spelled out what we already knew:

- Radical prostatectomy *can* be a source of cure for Stage A and B cases if they are caught early, but cures are not too frequent.
- Metastasis to the bone is often palliated by hormonal manipulation, including orchiectomy, but even that offers a five-year survival rate of only 21 percent.
- Although chemotherapy may be indicated for palliative effects, it should not be expected to extend life or to effectively control the disease.
- Metastasis, if it occurs, is inexorable and irreversible.

Bob is particularly helpful to Martha. Stan gives it to us straight, but Martha, always hopeful, focuses on the few positive aspects of his evaluation. Bob gets very specific and real. Yesterday, she went to see him for her nagging arthritis, and then, as he is prone to do, he took time to visit with her.

Bob underscored again that someday this cancer is going to get Chuck. I guess I felt the orchiectomy would stop any further metastasis for a long time. I never knew what "long" meant, but I'm sure in my mind it meant a LONG time. I was relieved that his PSA was down, but my rational and emotional acceptance hadn't come together. I could talk rationally about how the cancer was slowed down, but emotionally I wasn't as good. Whether it was Bob's talking to me or whether it was my reason and my emotions finally meshing, I don't know, but after we talked, I seemed to be more able to put things into perspective.

I awakened one morning last week and felt so good. I felt I really accepted where we were. This week Chuck has had some discomfort in his neck, and I've been able to witness this without coming apart. I realized that a stiff neck could mean the tumor is pressing on his neck, but it could also come from sleeping in an awkward position. Up until last week, I was constantly feeling anxious and leery of any aches or tiredness Chuck experienced. I realize now that I can't jump to conclusions when I don't know what's going on and that my anxiety won't change a thing. There are going to be lots of times when an ache or tiredness appears, and to be anxious will keep me—and

Chuck, because he knows me so well–tense and on edge. As I have prayed, I have felt such strength pouring into me because I have–once more–affirmed the cancer.

It has been very difficult for Chuck and me to watch Tom Meadows struggle. There's nothing more we want to do than minister to Tom and Terry, and that we're trying to do. When we see them, though, it shakes and depresses us, not only because we don't want this to be happening to them, but also because it reminds us that someday we'll be dealing with a cancer that gets away. It tears my heart out to think that Chuck will suffer like Tom.

AUGUST 23, 1989

From time to time we hear about someone who has "fought" cancer for many years. It's too easy to consider the fight to be in gigantic terms–a titanic struggle against the disease in its most advanced form, when treatment is profound, pain intense, deterioration inexorable.

Until recently, I had not considered the concept of the early fight–dealing with fear and anxiety, inchoate flagging of energy, and feelings of vulnerability and insecurity. Those are the quiet concerns of cancer that come even during the good days, and it's a subtle fight that must be carried on. It's another chance for affirmation to be effective. No place for denial or stoicism.

AUGUST 30, 1989

Martha and I are grateful for the open and forthright way in which we are able to talk about what we feel and think. But today I went too far, and I feel bad about it.

We were walking though the men's department at Marshall Field's. We stopped to admire a leather jacket for sale at $295. It was beautiful, and Martha would have been delighted if I'd purchased it, but I didn't, and as I walked away I said, "You know, I've not said this to you before, but given my uncertain future, it doesn't make sense for me to make a major purchase of an item I really don't need."

That was too much. It didn't need to be said. Martha's reply was poignant: "I know you feel that way, but honey, you don't want to be 'grundy' for the next ten years." Tears welled up in her eyes. I fell all over myself assuring her I had no intention of appearing grundy in the future. My comment had been that I saw little sense in a *major purchase* of an item *I didn't need.* Then I went on to say that I'd much rather she have the money for her needs and pleasure later. In frustration, she looked at me and said, "But I don't want the money. I want you."

My parents always taught me there are some things better left unsaid. I have not always been too skillful in following their advice, true though it is. It is impossible to unring a bell. Although Martha and I fully intend to continue our open and forthright style with one another, it's clear to me, under these circumstances in particular, that there *are* some things better left unsaid.

Keep that in mind, C.T. [Charles Taylor (Wheeler)]

AUGUST 31, 1989

This morning Martha and I talked about the jacket incident once more, because it points up again the issue of how much we say to one another. Surely there are things better left unsaid, but there is much to recommend sharing personal and private thoughts with one another, no matter how much anxiety they provoke. Conversely, there can be great harm in constantly internalizing difficult thoughts and feelings. I don't know if we'll ever solve these contradictions to our satisfaction. I guess we can expect each other to share, and I guess we can also expect the sharing to sometimes bring hurt and pain to both of us.

SEPTEMBER 22, 1989

Tom Meadows died today.

OCTOBER 24, 1989

After spending much of the night on the heat pad, trying to bring some comfort to my painful back and wondering if the pain is due to arthritis or cancer, I couldn't help getting a glimpse of what the progression of this disease must be like. A flashback to a day I asked Tom Meadows, "How goes it, Tom?" His reply was, "Oh, my back, my back." His pain was intense. My back pain is manageable with aspirin and heat, and its acuteness is intermittent but undeniable.

OCTOBER 28, 1989

I lunched with a dear friend of mine, Larry, who, after a ten-year battle, finally lost his wife, Marie, to cancer. Something had told me to call him. Gosh, he's hurting. They had lived for one another almost exclusively, so there are few people he can turn to for help and support, or so he believes. He did talk to me for two and a half hours, and it helped me immensely to hear him out, accept his grief and tears, and get a glimpse of the agony Martha will eventually face and endure.

I asked Larry how I could be most helpful to Martha. His answer was to talk everything through, to share our concerns and fears, and if we err, to err on the side of too much rather than too little. He spoke with considerable emotion of the times Marie hid her fears from him, sometimes even concealing that she had undergone certain medical tests, reporting the results to him after the fact. He talked about his sense of confusion when she would resist going somewhere or doing something on some superficial pretext, hiding the real reason.

I continue to wrestle with the issue of how much to say to Martha, but this evidence once again points up the need to express everything–sensitively, of course–but completely. Better to bear the pain of burdening the other than to let the loved one conjure up pictures that may be worse than the facts.

NOVEMBER 8, 1989

Guilt nags at me over the collapse of our sex life. When we do try to make love, we go through the motions, but it is largely unsatisfactory. I actually find myself resisting the idea of even trying. It takes two to tango, and I can't dance.

We have lots of physical contact, frequently holding each other, holding hands, and touching one another. It's amazing how much satisfaction we gain from these simple acts. Yet I feel I'm being less than I could be to Martha. But, bless her heart, she doesn't complain, and when I address the issue, she says, "That's OK. I get lots of satisfaction just holding you." She's trying to help me, I know, but it doesn't help much.

DECEMBER 8, 1989

I resist denial so much it's almost an obsession. A friend of mine literally denied his cancer, and continued to do so until a day or so before he died. His wife had to withdraw from his presence to cry and couldn't talk with him because of his obdurate attitude. Now, four years later, she continues to grieve because she was never permitted to say goodbye to him. Denial denies healing.

Martha and I know healing, not in the sense of cure, but in the sense of peace.

DECEMBER 19, 1989

On December 6, Chuck had his three-month check-up with Stan and told him about the pain in his back. Since that time, Bob has put him on Voltaren, which is the anti-inflammatory I take for arthritis. Thank heavens, it takes the edge off his discomfort. Chuck said the discomfort used to be now and then, but now he's aware of it when he moves different ways. He doesn't complain, but I sense his discomfort and feel helpless to do anything about it.

I do affirm Chuck's cancer, but I'm not as good at affirming his discomfort. I have a difficult time accepting his pain. He has done so well for the past three and a half years, and I want him to continue for many more. There's nothing that says he won't, but I am so threatened because I love him so much.

Even though we're both on Voltaren, I don't think of myself as taking pain medication, but rather as being on a medication for arthritis. When Chuck first said he was taking pain medication, I objected, as it sounded too foreboding to me. After much conversation, I realize what Voltaren really is and accept the fact that it's OK to say "pain medication." It's interesting how I react to anything that even hints at Chuck's cancer acting up.

It's a beautiful Christmas season. We're going to be with Tom and Carol in Washington and are eagerly looking forward to the occasion. Every Christmas season is stirring, and every Christmas has special meaning as it makes us all aware of what Jesus came to tell us—the good news of God's love.

JANUARY 9, 1990

My friend Pat died right after Christmas. He lasted only two years after his diagnosis. His prostate cancer had been inoperable–stage D at diagnosis. As recently as August 1988, his PSA had been reduced to 2.8 by virtue of an orchiectomy, but by March it was rising. Flutamide in May failed to slow it down. I talked with him from time to time during these two years. He was often apprehensive and anxious, but always hopeful.

And George died last week. He and I had been buddies for forty years. Fourteen months ago his PSA was 200, and metastasis had advanced to his hip, shoulder, and ribs. By May of last year, he was experiencing extensive metastasis, and from November it was all downhill. His kidneys finally failed, and he was overwhelmed.

Martha and I stayed close to George and Barbara. While I know he appreciated the relationship, I don't have much confidence that I was all that helpful to him. He and Barb believed this was God's will, and they submitted to it. Their technical understanding of the progress of the disease was limited, and their hostility to those who were unable to control its progress was evident. They were convinced of the efficacy of his unorthodox treatment, which made it hard to relate to them, but I listened and tried to be supportive.

So two of my buddies are gone within the last couple of weeks. I was emotionally overcome and reduced to tears by the news of George's death, scared for myself and Martha. I don't want Martha to have to endure such experiences, but we have no acceptable choice, and we are confronted–again–with the necessity to trust God for strength to endure and for patience to withstand.

There is such a feeling of helplessness. We can't remove these events from the scene, but what we can do is to affirm this darkness and make of the whole experience something worthwhile for ourselves and others. We continue to learn more about affirming the darkness, and as we do, it gives us feelings of soaring in flight. So although we are unable to hold off the ravages of cancer, we insist on living a balanced life. Total positiveness and total negativity are both unrealistic.

JANUARY 26, 1990

Following Bob's directive, Martha and I continue to walk four miles a day. Yesterday I pushed myself, though, and did nearly eight miles. Martha needed the car, so I walked home from the barber shop and then walked to the church, in addition to the four-mile junket we took together in the early morning.

I wondered how far I could go and what the consequences of a longer walk might be. Today, to my delight, I seem none the worse for wear, and I am encouraged.

JANUARY 27, 1990

Hallelujah! We made love. What more needs to be said?

FEBRUARY 13, 1990

As I haven't written since Christmas, I must say that the holiday was everything we had hoped for and more! It was so good to be with our families, plus Carol's mother and Doug's parents; that made a full house for Tom and Carol. Carol pulled out all the stops. The house was beautifully decorated, the food bountiful and delicious, and everyone was made comfortable and most welcomed. It really is quite a treat when families can get along, complete with in-laws on all sides, and the atmosphere is filled with caring, not contention. We're all so fortunate that we all respect, as well as like, one another.

Chuck and I had recently a beautiful experience with Karen. She came to spend his birthday weekend with us, and it made a very special sixty-ninth birthday for Chuck. Now Karen didn't come because she was afraid her dad wouldn't have a seventieth birthday. She wanted to follow her "nudge" and her need to really see how Dad and I were doing. As she said, she can talk on the phone, but she wanted to see with her own eyes and experience us. It was superb! It was evident to me that she and Chuck had a lot they wanted to share. Much of what Chuck told her we had already discussed on the four miles we walk each day. He shared his writings with her, and of course "Herman," the wood carving he is creating for her. I didn't feel left out in any way; I was so grateful they could share as they did.

One of the great privileges I had this weekend was rubbing hearts with Karen about her feelings in dealing with her dad's cancer. I know how I felt when my dad had it, and how it hurt. She's always so sensitive in talking with me and finding out how I am that I wanted to reach out to her, to tell her I knew how it felt when it was my dad, and I wanted her to feel free to tell me about her hurt. I didn't want her to fall "between the cracks." People minister to the spouse of the person with cancer, but Karen has needs, too. Through all this discussion, Chuck was sitting across the room listening. Karen and I hadn't closeted ourselves away from his ears. I wasn't sure if she

would feel comfortable talking in Chuck's presence, but she was, and
it turned out to be a great sharing for all of us.

The weekend went so fast. We went to Couple's Circle, where
it was great to show Karen off; we walked through several new
buildings downtown and shopped in the new City Center
Mall; we went to the cemetery and placed a single yellow rose
on Martha's mother's grave, as it was the first anniversary of her
death; we worshipped together. Spontaneously Karen prayed at
the dinner table on my birthday, a beautiful and moving prayer
from deep in her being. We lost a lot of sleep to nocturnal conversations, but after taking Karen to the airport for a late afternoon flight, we returned home, had dinner, and were in bed
and asleep before she landed in Boston.

The recurrent conversation during Karen's visit was around
cancer. It was actually anticipatory grieving, not morbid, but a
healthy expression of feeling. I suspect few people are able or
willing to engage in such a conversation. Karen said, "I can
accept death, Dad; I can accept your death, but I can't accept
the idea of life without you."

Martha answered, "Karen, I remember so vividly the deterioration and death of my own father, and I can identify with
you and feel your anguish." I talked about my conviction of
the importance of life's quality, as opposed to its quantity, and
of the difficulty of contemplating the stress and hurt Martha,
Tom, and Karen will feel as they preside over the days of my
decline and death.

Each of us openly grieved, and I thanked Martha and Karen
for letting me *have* cancer. So few people will let me have it. They
ignore it, never mention it to me (or perhaps ask their questions
of Martha out of my earshot), deny it, or dismiss it with offhand
comments. It is as if they are unwilling to let me have what I
have. I have cancer. I know I have cancer. I have been advised of
its inexorable progress and its ultimate result. I have accepted it.
But most people will not or cannot meet me where I am.
Martha, Tom, and Karen do. A mere handful of others do—but,
oh, so few. And when I am with someone who does, I have to
guard myself carefully so as not to inundate that person with it.

Karen gave Martha and me an insight that helps us understand others' responses. She pointed out that the passage of

time is a positive sign for most cancer patients, a cause for rejoicing. We understand and accept the fact that the hormonal approach to my disease is temporary and is almost certain to dissipate in its effectiveness. Thus, in my case, the longer we go, the closer we come to my deterioration. The conventional wisdom most people embrace is that if one survives cancer for five years, one is cured, and now that I have four years behind me, they think I've just about got it made when, in fact, the opposite is true. Others don't understand this, and we become uncomfortable in the face of their increasing optimism.

A tremendously helpful perspective from Karen!

FEBRUARY 17, 1990

Yesterday, I passed blood in my urine.

> That caught our attention *immediately*. Chuck called Stan's office only to find he was out of town. His nurse suggested we come over to the clinic and one of his staff would work Chuck in. Dr. Y. did a cytoscopy and found no abnormality. We're grateful for that but are still in the dark about the reason for the blood, so the next step was to order an IVP—an x-ray of the kidneys. It was scheduled for the next Tuesday.

FEBRUARY 26, 1990

The IVP was negative. The PSA was within normal limits. The source of the blood? Unknown. Perhaps, Stan thinks, it's residual from my surgery. We were prepared for the worst. We were prepared for the eventuality that this was the beginning of the breakdown of the hormonal treatment. It seemed to us this would constitute a very early breakdown, although we have been advised a breakdown is almost certainly inevitable.

So it was another ten days of limbo. We handled it better than previous limbos, but it was not without its stress. We told a few people, needing to share it with someone, and that, of course, stirred them up. In hindsight we wonder if it isn't in our interest (and our friends') to be a little more reserved, not revealing very much until we know more. How many times can friends be expected to respond when we cry wolf? Our kids, yes, but our friends? We delude ourselves when we think we can tell only one or two. The caring network comes into play, and they tell one another.

On the other hand, it is so very supportive to be cared for by loving people. It's a dilemma.

MARCH 9, 1990

Recently I read a short article about coping with crisis; it summarized a study of a group of people diagnosed with cancer. One-third of the people had experienced some degree of depression. The other two-thirds revealed several common characteristics. They sought information from community resources or publications; they had a sense of usefulness, not dependence; and they had frequent contact with close friends, with whom they were completely open about their condition. My experience heartily confirms the conclusions of this study. All three of these responses have been enormously helpful to me. Coping is important, first with the idea of the disease and then with the disease itself.

APRIL 10, 1990

The other day, Karen called three times. She said a lot of things to me that reflect her acute awareness of the importance of saying what's in one's heart while it can be said. She had been referring to her Bible in response to a comment I'd made about a particular passage I had read at church. While handling the Bible, she found several notes I wrote to her years ago in which I commented on the belief Martha and I had in her and her capabilities. Her phone calls today were simply to say thank-you for those words from long ago and to acknowledge that she feels and always has felt our support.

There are so many things we need to do and so many things we need to say when we get into a crunch. Unless we have rehearsed them and dealt with them in earlier days, we can expect to be helpless. No one knows what his or her response will be to the ultimate crunch, but I can imagine that ours, as a family, will be emotional and expressive.

APRIL 16, 1990

Sometimes we feel as if we might better delude ourselves into denial, to look the other way, to attempt to ignore, but we know the pain of that is far worse than the pain of walking squarely into the darkness, so we don't. Our many conversations, however, are not without stress. Our revelations to one another of our physical and emotional feelings are not always comforting, but after talking them through, we feel better and closer and more accepting of everything about this disease.

Sometimes there is the dilemma of how to launch the conversation. What shall we say? How and when shall we say it? For each of us there is always a hesitation that must be overcome before we are able to get into the conversation for which we both long and in which we have such confidence.

On our trip to Florida, we talked a lot, first on an early morning walk in Charleston, West Virginia, and later as we drove along the highway. We compared ourselves, both physically and emotionally, to where we perceived ourselves to have been three months, six months, and twelve months ago. Martha commented that I seem increasingly introspective and give more evidence of discomfort, fatigue, and weakness. I believe her perception is accurate, and in addition, I perceive that I feel more anxiety for Martha when we are apart. I revealed to Martha that she is increasingly "clingy" and seems to want to maximize our time together. She too seems more introspective and contemplative. We talked about this trip and how we both had an increasingly uncertain view of the probability of such a trip next year and the year thereafter. We talked about dying and commented that life itself is a fatal disease.

After four years, life is good and we are grateful. We are closer than ever, having traveled this road with openness and honesty, steering a course directly into the wind (although Martha's tack is sometimes a bit more tangential to the wind than mine). Martha experiences a whole range of feelings, and like me, she attempts to protect me from some of them.

APRIL 18, 1990

We knew as soon as we came back from Florida that we'd have the bone scan to face. The doctor who read the scan invited us back to his office to explain it to us and to compare it to last year's. He was happy to tell us that the spot on Chuck's spine, at the neck, had not changed size, nor had the one on his lower back; however, a new spot has appeared in his lower spine. Since the others have not changed, the hope is that the orchiectomy will hold this one in check too. It seems odd to be happy that only one new spot appeared, but we are. We really feel as if we have a new lease on life.

MAY 15, 1990

Four years ago today Jack told me I had cancer. After four years, life is good and we are grateful, but on this fourth anniversary, I feel as if I am skating out onto a frozen lake with full knowledge that the ice is getting thinner. And the farther I skate, the thinner the ice will become, and one fair day, I know the ice will give way and I will slip through.

My back continues to be a source of discomfort—growing gradually, oh, so gradually, but inexorably. Last Sunday I served the chalice at communion, and in so doing—being required to bend over to serve the kneeling communicants—my lower back responded with real pain, for the first time more than simple discomfort. Although the pain subsided after communion, it was such that I broke out into a profuse sweat. It startled me, and an extreme feeling of helplessness and loneliness came over me.

The fatigue, the leg weakness, and the discomfort in my back all contribute to my feeling of being on thin ice, but my spirits are just great and I am loving life. I can even venture the opinion that cancer, if one must have it, is a gift. It slows us down enough to be contemplative and to value life's most precious aspects, to know and to love each other more deeply and in ways probably known only by those who are vulnerable and threatened. Such people, if they are lovers and friends, live their lives differently, and amid the pain of impending uncertainty they come to see and experience life from a new and rich perspective.

We hate it and we love it. A contradiction? Sure, but that's where the truth is found.

MAY 25, 1990

It is atypical that I dream about cancer, but I had a dream that was vivid and real, sufficiently so as to awaken me and cause me to pray. In my dream, Karen was with me. She was ill at ease, withdrawn, and quiet. I urged her to reveal her feelings, and she stated reluctantly that she was afraid. She didn't want me to die.

I like to think that my response to her in the dream was not typical of me. Perhaps it was, at least in part, the reason I woke up in such distress. In the dream, rather than enter into her feelings with her, I found myself trying to talk her out of them. I didn't want her to hurt, and obviously I didn't want to hurt with her.

I woke and prayed for insight into how I might meet the needs of loved ones who stand by, watching. I knew as I prayed that one can never avoid the hurt of being the watcher, and that part of being ill is to reach out and calm the fears of those who watch, to enter into the anxieties that crowd *their* dreams, to hurt and feel for and with them. In my dream and prayer, I had a vivid glimpse of what is to come and clear insight as to how I might best respond.

JUNE 27, 1990

In a talk at First Community Village recently, Stan dropped what to us was a startling statistic. He said that three years after an orchiectomy for metastasis, 50 percent of patients are dead, and only 10 percent will be alive after ten years. Being nearly two years post-orchiectomy, I didn't receive this news without its getting my attention.

So we welcomed today's visit with Stan. The discomfort in my back continues, and the leg weakness and fatigue are unabated. I reported this to Stan and for the first time also told him I had fallen several times in the last three or four months. I attribute the falls to the weakness in my legs.

Stan revealed that my PSA is currently 3.4, and while this seems to me to be a marked increase from the 2.5 of four months ago, Stan, with no detectable concern, said (a) we might expect some PSA fluctuations, and (b) there is no further treatment indicated at this time. He referred me to Bob concerning the falls and suggested a CT scan of the brain and some blood work.

> We have heard time and time again, in one context or another, that we were entering a crucial period. Each time we see him now, Stan says radiation or chemotherapy will be in store if Chuck's PSA soars or his back causes more pain or a combination of both. We know that more treatment is down the road. How will we handle it? The same way we've been doing. We'll live each day to its fullest; we'll do things that feed our bliss; we'll hug and kiss and keep on being ourselves.

JUNE 28, 1990

One day last week Martha asked me if I was discouraged. Initially I denied it, but then I denied being encouraged either. As we talked, we concluded that our feelings about all of this were often at cross-purposes. How can one walk into the darkness with courage and hope and still feel discouraged? Perhaps my concept of walking into the darkness that way denies me the right to a whole range of feelings, contradictory though they may be.

Martha also experiences a full gamut of feelings, and like me, she tries to protect me from some of them. Our experiences are uniquely ours and essentially different. We face different futures, and we know, as with almost no other experience since our marriage, that we will have to walk into and through the future alone, without our mutual support. No one can die for me, and no one can be a widow for Martha.

JUNE 29, 1990

How sweet it is when one's mood changes and things seem not nearly so dark. For the past couple of days I really expected to shuffle off in the next year or two. Today things are not nearly so grim. As a matter of fact, if someone were to ask me if I expected to die in the next year or two, I think my answer would be, "Maybe, but then maybe not." That's a whole lot better, and today I found real humor in a comment Tom made the other evening. We had called to bring him up to date on my visit to Stan, and we talked with him about my pending work-up to seek the reason for my persistent fatigue, leg weakness, and falling. We told Tom that Stan had said I might be having some TIAs [transient ischemic attacks].

Said Tom humorously, "Hey, Dad, you can't die of a heart attack or a stroke; you're writing a book about cancer!" We keep finding humor, and we hope we always will.

JULY 8, 1990

We're in limbo again. So what's new? We've concluded we'll be in limbo the rest of our lives, waiting for an appointment, test results, or further developments to manifest themselves. I think we handle limbo better as time passes, but there is still a build-up of stress, and we react to stress differently, each to the discomfort of the other.

> I become preoccupied, and Chuck withdraws as he tries to work things out in his mind. When this happens, we get out of communication. In my preoccupation, I say things that aren't well thought out or that aren't "me." Chuck becomes very nit-picky, and that isn't him. When he withdraws, I feel as though he's unhappy with something I've done or said, or he's keeping something from me. We finally talk it through, and after our talk, we're usually back to normal.

Three cheers for talking. We're getting pretty adept at it, thank God.

JULY 11, 1990

Chuck's brain scan was normal, thank God. Though Stan had said nothing about a tumor, both Chuck and I had thought about it, but it wasn't until Bob mentioned the possibility that we talked about it. The idea of a brain tumor upset us both more than we thought it had, and we were both relieved at the report.

JULY 23, 1990

It's crazy! My back has been so bad the past three days, and today it feels just great. Sometimes I feel like a yo-yo.

AUGUST 5, 1990

As my cancer progresses, Martha resists the symptoms. She doesn't deny them exactly, but she resists them. "If only they would go away," she seems to say. Most recently it has been the increasing lack of stamina, fatigue, and weakness in my legs. I am convinced that this weakness is the source of my unsteadiness and falling. I find myself touching some stationary object as I pass by, sitting longer and easier, seeking a more comfortable chair or a reclining position. I require more sleep, and when I waken after nine or ten hours, my legs feel as if they need even more sleep. They feel weak.

> Part of my problem with Chuck's fatigue is that it's a sign the cancer is working. I remember how fatigued my dad was when he had cancer, and it concerns me about Chuck. We were out for dinner with friends the other night, and it was apparent that Chuck was very tired. I feel guilty that I complained about his getting up from the

table before I was finished, as he needed to sit in a more comfortable chair.

I understand, I really do. There's nothing I want more than for Chuck to feel comfortable. I don't want him to hurt or be fatigued. I guess it's my way of trying to deny that anything is wrong, that everything is normal—just the same as usual.

I realize, as I always seem to do when I finally recognize I'm in denial, that life is so good and that we've been so lucky to enjoy these four years together. I realize how fortunate we are. I want nothing more than for Chuck to feel he doesn't need to put up a front at home. This is the place for him to let down, if that's what he wants to do. I want life to be as normal as possible with neither of us putting on false faces. We just want to be us, and that means that at times we'll show hurt or anxiety for one another, but that's love. I'll never mind paying the price for being so much in love for all these nearly forty-seven years.

Before he died, my friend Pat used to complain of leg weakness. He asked me if I experienced it. At the time I said no. He was puzzled by it, and it caused him great concern. I think about that now.

AUGUST 8, 1990

This week, Chuck gave me a beautiful wooden cross he whittled for me to wear around my neck. It is such a work of art, such a work of love. As I look at it, I can visualize him sitting in his black leather chair, whittling away with all the patience in the world. It is a joy to watch him whittle. I really am so emotional as I try to tell my feelings about being presented with such a loving gift. The cross has two entwined circles near the bottom. We don't know what those mean officially, but for us they stand for our love and our lives, which are so intertwined. The cross has great meaning for us, not only the cross itself, but also what we call "the other side of the cross." By that we mean all that happened after Christ died on the cross—eternal life, the Holy Spirit, and, of course, forgiveness. The cross is a symbol from which much strength comes. It is a reminder that one is never alone. I am so proud of my cross and will wear it with gratitude for the love Chuck and I have. I will always feel that love when I wear it.

AUGUST 13, 1990

Our experience with cancer must be vastly different from that of many others. First, because we insist on being informed participants, I suspect we understand what is happening to us far more clearly than do most people. We are deeply appreciative of the openness and frankness of our principal physicians. A couple of days ago I talked with an acquaintance who had had prostate surgery but is almost totally in the dark, because his urologist is one who tells his patients almost nothing, nor does he arm them with any statistical support to help them interpret their feelings. As we talked, I wondered what my friend thinks about in the middle of the night. What do he and his wife say to one another? What does she think about? What do they cry about?

Second, while this journal was and is intended to be a record of one man's fight against cancer which I hope will be of value and reassurance to those who follow, it also has several ancillary values. It is one of my methods of coping. It is in keeping with my need to write down what is important. It enables me to discover how I feel about what is happening to us, to record it with as much objectivity and honesty as I can muster. In addition, one of the unintended and unexpected benefits of the journal is the fact that I am laying down a record to which we can refer as time passes and the disease progresses.

I have gone back in these readings and reviewed where we were—three, six, twelve months ago—and have compared how I feel now to what I recorded then. One soon forgets how one felt at some point in the past or what he was thinking or doing. But to read about it is to be assisted in recollection and in making comparisons.

Martha saw Bob today, and he commented to her that he had written to Stan of his findings in the various tests—that he couldn't identify any reasons for my fatigue and weakness other than the progression of cancer. He said, "You know, Martha, one can't detect any perceptible change from day to day, but when one looks back over a period of months, the change is more apparent."

Three cheers, then, for this journal and the unexpected ways it is helping us. It seems to me that if I were a physician, I'd urge all my cancer patients to keep a journal for their own edification.

OCTOBER 10, 1990

I haven't written in my journal since August. There have been many things to write about, but I couldn't get it together, as Chuck was having a hard summer. It was a revelation to me to see how well he handled our trip to visit friends in Arizona and Denver. Fortunately he was not having what he calls "the whoopsies," so his balance was better; his legs were still weak, though, some days more than others.

There is a hill we traverse every morning on our walk, and I can tell if he's going to have difficulty with fatigue by how easily he climbs that hill. There are mornings he starts off real well and then tires before we get home. We walk at whatever pace is best for him. Although it's apparent he's very tired when we arrive home, that's OK. It's just great to have him walking with me.

Two months is a long to time for me to refrain from writing. I suspect that the fact I didn't write says as much as I might have, had I written.

It was a long period of limbo. I didn't feel at all well. As time passed, I began to feel better, although the waning of my energy and my leg weakness persisted. We became more aware than ever of the necessity of living to protect me, so far as possible, from fatigue and stress—not easy for a couple of habitually active people. I now need eight to ten hours of sleep, and I find myself supplementing that with naps. I have abandoned my enjoyable practice of rising at 5:00 a.m. to write and read. When 5:00 a.m. comes, my motivation is too low to get my head up off the pillow.

We had been scheduled for my checkup on October 24, but when Stan's office called to change it to today, I was delighted. I needed to get a PSA update and Stan's interpretation of these developments. It had been a long, gradual build-up of limbo since I saw him in June, punctuated by days that were good but not as good as they had been. It seemed to me some deterioration had occurred, and I wanted to quantify it. So we went to the new cancer hospital—the Arthur G. James Cancer Hospital and Research Institute—with a certain hesitation but with eager anticipation.

We walked into the shiny, new twelve-story, 160-bed hospi-

tal, and as we sat in the waiting room of the outpatient department, I realized that everyone else there also had cancer. I was
reminded of the insidious nature of the disease. All these people looked good, but inside they were slowly being eaten up, as
I am. No wonder people who understand so little often say to
me, "Gosh, you sure *look* good."

My PSA is up to 3.9. Stan said that my weakness and fatigue
are manifestations of the progress of cancer; that the increase
in the PSA confirms the progression; and that the next phase
of treatment will relate to the advance of the PSA while also
controlling the pain. That phase will probably involve
Flutamide or chemotherapy. I asked about the effectiveness of
chemo. Everything I've read from the NCI indicates it's of little value. Stan agreed, but said it's often effective in controlling
pain. He concluded by saying we should buy more time. As
long as my pain can be controlled by my current medication,
he would prefer to do no more, and he commented that the
next phase is often accompanied by toxicity and other side
effects. He gave us another four months before further evaluation unless my symptoms require me to see him sooner.

I feel today that I am truly in the grip of this disease, that it
is slowly consuming me. I identify with Martha's father, as I
recall watching him helplessly succumb to the inexorable
march of his cancer. It seems as if it's a gradual letdown, each
event representing a slippage—not much, just a little, but clearly slippage. I have enormous gratitude and appreciation for
Stan—a good man. And I have such feelings for Martha, too,
and for the way she travels this painful road beside me, with
never a complaint, always a pleasant word, totally flexible,
always responsive to my needs and wishes. What a person!
What a marriage! I sure stumbled into this one. How can a person be as blessed as I am?

> I feel so grateful the report was good. What more could we want,
> except the impossible, like a cure? We have a reprieve for four more
> months, and at this point I'll take every reprieve that comes along. It's
> great to know we can keep on living and enjoying each day. That we
> are doing.

OCTOBER 22, 1990

This is the sixteen-hundredth good day since my original surgery. We can only say, "Hallelujah and thanks be to God!"

We saw Stan at a banquet the other night. What a guy! He's got only one string on his fiddle—cancer. He lives it and is immersed in it, seemingly to the exclusion of all else. We have such warm feelings for him. He told Martha we are an inspiration in the way in which we deal with my cancer. To some degree this may be b.s., but it made us feel good.

OCTOBER 23, 1990

Thanks to Tom's encouraging her to deal with life ahead, Martha is finding benefit in talking about my death. It hurts, but she can talk, and that's good.

The other morning as we walked, we talked about how things will be after I die. We talked about her feelings about marrying again, her traveling, and about what she might do to follow her bliss, to feed her soul. These were not new thoughts to her. Obviously she had pondered them for some time, but it was a new experience for each of us to have her articulate them. It felt good; we both thought the conversation was helpful.

Last Sunday, I served the chalice at church, and after having knelt to receive communion, I struggled, I guess, to stand. My leg weakness was evident. Michael Jupin, our warm and sensitive rector, said to me quietly, "Chuck, you may take my arm any time it is difficult for you to rise." That simple statement meant so much to me—first, that he was aware of my situation, and second, that he was willing to be helpful. It made it seem all right to have this difficulty, and that there is no need to feel embarrassed or to attempt to hide it from others.

These experiences are all part of affirming the darkness.

OCTOBER 30, 1990

Tom and Karen have both been here this month. Tom wrote after he returned to D.C. His letter commented on the guilt I feel about hurting Martha and the kids when I openly discuss my thoughts and feelings. He stated his wish that I assume no responsibility for their hurt, but that I let them hurt and deal with it themselves.

Many years ago, when Tom was responding to the anxieties we had for him, we were advised by a physician to let him live his own life, removing from him much of the anxiety-oriented direction we had been imposing–to let him live with the consequences of his own choices. During that period, I left Tom alone on the curb of Redding Road, a busy thoroughfare, on a dark and murky night. He had indicated he was too tired to finish our walk home and had asked me to carry him. He was only seven years old, and leaving him there on the curb when it was within my power (and my desire) to pick him up was one of the most difficult things I ever did.

In Tom's letter, he urged me to let Martha "cross Redding Road alone." His comment was so very apt. This whole experience is existential. No one can take your bath for you.

NOVEMBER 7, 1990

These have been pretty good days. For the past two weeks I've felt really good. Our calendar has been full, and we've had a lot of evening activity, but I've still done well. Leg weakness and fatigue persist, but I can live with these. Back pain is intermittent, but there's no need to supplement the Voltaren with Tylenol. Great!

And then today the roof fell in. Martha has a brain tumor which must be operated on. How much more must she endure? She says growing old isn't for sissies, and that's the truth. We will affirm this new darkness together as we have the previous darkness, but right now we are both devastated. We feel pulverized. Tomorrow we'll begin again.

NOVEMBER 14, 1990

Martha's surgery was scheduled for November 19, but they called today and rescheduled it for November 28. Her neurosurgeon wants more time for evaluation of tests and consultation with his team and partners. He's going to be out of town for a few days and feels crowded under the initial schedule. We dislike the additional wait but want him to take all the time he needs to prepare for this delicate procedure.

I wrote on November 7 how good I've been feeling, and this has continued on into this period of stress. Such pain as I have has been covered nearly completely by Voltaren and without heat. It looks to me as if the adrenaline flowing in my system is a good treatment for cancer. Perhaps no one has ever thought of it. Ha ha.

NOVEMBER 21, 1990

This is our forty-seventh wedding anniversary, a different one to say the least. A dark cloud hangs over this day. Martha's neurosurgeon spoke very explicitly on Monday. It will be no picnic. He says the surgery will last at least nine hours and could take as long as twenty. I'm afraid. She's afraid.

NOVEMBER 1990 (events recollected in February 1991)

On November 7, Chuck and I took our daily three-to-four mile walk, ending up at Bob's office for the reports of my physical and brain scan. I had been experiencing a tingling on the right side of my face and some numbness around my mouth for about a year, and after some unsuccessful attempts to alleviate it, it seemed prudent to have the scan. When we arrived at the office, it became quite apparent something was amiss. When we looked at the scan, there was a tumor, bright as could be. Bob referred us to Dr. Hal, and fortunately we were able to make an appointment for the next day.

Chuck and I finished our walk home in a state of shock. We immediately called Michael Jupin, who came and sat with us for a couple of hours. He didn't try to make us feel better or say the right thing. He merely supported us and let us share our thoughts and fears. His prayer gave us peace.

The following day we saw the neurosurgeon, who told us I had an acoustic neuroma* that had affected the facial nerves and the right optic nerve. The good news was that such tumors are benign, but the surgery would be very delicate and involved. It would take twelve-to-eighteen hours, and the risks would be substantial. For openers, there was the possibility that I would hemorrhage or that the right side of my face would sag because of damage to the nerves. In addition, my right eye might not close, which would mean the eyelid might have to be weighted or sewn shut. I definitely would be deaf in my right ear, and because there was involvement of the brain stem, I might have difficulty with swallowing, motor activity, and other functions.

---

* A benign tumor which develops from the auditory nerve and grows inside the auditory channel. It can cause progressive hearing loss, headache, facial numbness, dizziness, and unsteady gait. Difficulty in speaking and swallowing may occur in a later stage.

All these were possibilities, not probabilities, except for the loss of hearing, and that was not hard to accept to rid myself of the tumor. Of course, as the doctor said, "Sometimes the operation is a success, but the patient doesn't survive." All this gave Chuck and me lots to think about and pray about. These were difficult days, and we "hunkered down." We were both filled with fear, consumed with fear, but along with the fear there was faith.

It became clear *again* that we have very different ways of coping. Chuck deals with each possibility in depth and needs to talk about it. I deal with the possibilities, never denying them, but after I've dealt with them, I don't want to talk about them anymore. I turn then to the happy side—in this case, the aftermath of surgery. I know what can happen, but I'll deal with that if and when. I hurt Chuck one evening when I said I was the only one holding out any hope. It wasn't true, but that's what I heard when he talked about what might happen or said everything would be OK, no matter what. We were both terribly uptight. Since then we've talked about our different ways of coping, and we understand.

On November 27, Karen flew in from Boston to be with us. I went into Riverside Hospital that day. Late in the afternoon, Michael Jupin brought communion to us in the hospital. His wife, Barbara, came with him. It was a true gesture of love for her to come, and I was touched. Michael offered a healing service with the communion that had Chuck, Karen, Barbara, and me in tears. The service was so calming and, as always, gave us peace. Michael asked me what my breath prayer [a short, personal prayer] was, to which I answered, "God give me strength and courage." He told me that if I said that prayer the last thing before I lost consciousness, it would probably be the first thing I'd say when I came to. He added that he too would say my breath prayer on the day of surgery.

The anesthesiologist came in to tell me what to expect during the operation. We were thrilled to discover it was Dr. Maria S., who we knew from the Summit Chase condos, where we lived before now, and who we also knew had a terrific reputation at Riverside. I'd heard I would be on a respirator in surgery and might still be on it when I went to the neurosurgical intensive care unit (NICU). I wondered why. Maria explained how completely anesthetized I'd be, not even breathing on my own. Boy, I was glad Maria was the anesthesiologist!

Chuck and Karen left early so they could have dinner and get to bed, as they were due back at the hospital about 5:00 a.m. After they left, I was kept very busy while a shunt, which would be used for intravenous feeding and medication, was placed in my right side just below the shoulder. That was quite an experience, because they tried the left side for thirty minutes before switching to the right. It's a rather involved procedure, and to make sure the shunt is in the right place an x-ray is taken. Then I was given two units of plasma, which took a half hour, if not longer.

I settled down to sleep about 1:30 a.m. About 3:00 a.m., I wakened from a light sleep and realized how calm I was. Lying there, I thought of all the people who were praying for me. Even some people in South Carolina—who didn't know me but were part of a healing group to which our friends, the Vlceks, belong—were praying for me. In the three weeks we have been waiting, so many dear friends have come by or called to tell us they would pray for me. I have been praying for strength and courage, and I truly felt it.

Karen and Chuck arrived at the hospital at 5:15 and accompanied me to EEG, where I was strung up with sensors on my head, feet, and hands. I must have looked a sight! The purpose of all this was to let the surgeon know if he was cutting any nerves to my face while he extricated the tumor. I was in EEG for one and a half hours and then wheeled to surgery.

I had asked back in my room when I would have preoperative medication and was told in EEG. When I asked in EEG, they said before I went to surgery. As I was wheeled past my surgeon, I said I hadn't had anything, and he said I didn't need it now. Really I'm glad I didn't have it, because I was calm and had a terrific sense of well-being.

Looking about the operating room, I honestly felt as though I were in a cocoon—it was a warm feeling—and I felt as though God or the Holy Spirit was there. I had no fear, and I knew everything would be all right. I knew that whether my face sagged or I hemorrhaged or I died, it was OK. I was at peace, and the surgeon's hands were being guided. I said my breath prayer and that is all I remember.

I was on the operating table for nearly twelve hours and then in recovery, so it was almost midnight when I saw Chuck and Karen standing beside me in NICU. What a wonderful sight! Chuck was smiling from ear to ear, and he asked me to smile at him and to wink. I did all that, which showed him that the "awfuls" of a sagging face or an eyelid that wouldn't blink were not to be. How grateful we were! I had no idea what time it was; I only knew the operation was over and I could smile at Karen and Chuck and squeeze their hands. I kept telling them Tom was coming in on an airplane—it's funny the things that stick in your mind.

The first thing I remembered before seeing Chuck and Karen was my breath prayer. It happened just as Michael said it would.

I stayed in NICU the remainder of the night and until around 6:00 p.m. the next day. I have little recollection of time, but I do remember seeing Bob and Hal come in. The times when Chuck and Karen came were always special, and I clearly recall Karen helping me try some juice and then holding me up while I was sick from it. I'll always remember seeing her with my cross around her neck. That was special.

The nurses in NICU are so warm, efficient, and caring. It's a busy place filled with very ill patients, but each has his or her own nurse and one feels very at ease. When my doctor asked if I would like to go to my own room, I was delighted. I knew that meant I was doing OK, and I was thrilled to get to the new room.

I really don't remember much of that night, but I'll never forget Karen coming in the next day with a gorgeous basket brimming over with daisies. She is our daisy, and daisies are symbolic of her. It was difficult to see them through my tears. Chuck sat beside my bed as close as he could get. We held hands, and he read me the many wonderful cards and letters that had come. I could hardly wait for him to arrive that morning, to see me sitting up in bed and to know everything was going well. Almost the first thing Chuck did was to get a mirror and show me my scar and how much hair was left. I was happily surprised to see I had all my hair except the portion on the right side in the back, where the operation was performed.

It hardly seemed possible Karen was getting ready to go back to Boston. She came on Tuesday, and here it was Friday already. Friday afternoon Tom arrived. He and Karen overlapped one another by only a couple of hours, but it was great for them to have a short time with all of us together. When Tom came into my room, he leaped around the end of my bed with joy in his face, because he saw me whole and not with a lot of tubes sticking out of me and my face sagging.

It meant so much to me and Chuck to have Tom and Karen with us. One of the serendipities of this whole affair was that Chuck had time to be with each of the kids alone for four days. In that time, he was able to relate to them in a special way. They worried, they fretted, they rejoiced, they cried, they laughed, and they shared. It made me happy and content to watch them or to hear them over the phone. It was important to me that Chuck was taken care of, as this was terribly hard on him and he really didn't need the stress. Knowing Tom and Karen individually were with him gave me such comfort. I have written to each of them, but words are inadequate to express the love I have for them. Dear God, thank you!

One of the funny things that happened was my completely myopic view of what it meant to come home. To me it meant returning to *our apartment*, not to the health-care center or the clinic at the Village. When both doctors said I could come home, I was overjoyed but still fearful I might end up elsewhere than in our apartment. I called Chuck to tell him I was being released, and he said he'd call the clinic and tell them. Boy, did I get upset. I said in no uncertain terms that he was not going to mess anything up! And he didn't. When I got home, Chuck had signs all over the bedroom welcoming me. And I do have to say it was a good feeling to know there were clinic nurses on duty all the time and to have them check on me periodically.

In all this, Chuck has been so strong and, as always, so loving. He has put his own health problems aside. I was greatly concerned for him, but he juggled everything, including his own year-end work. I really disliked using our time together in this manner, but I soon realized what a special time it was: we were together, sharing everything, just the two of us. It was a blessed time!

The outpouring of love from our friends and church was overwhelming. For a full two weeks, the crisis network at St. Mark's brought dinner in to us. What delicious meals! Other friends also brought food, and it all helped Chuck so much. In addition, there were phone calls, cards, letters, and prayers. The beautiful aspect of all this was that the love and caring were for both of us, not just for me, the patient.

The entire experience has been humbling. How does one say thank-you? For sure, Chuck and I want to be part of the crisis network. I don't know how we go about it, but we want to give to others what was given to us.

It's impossible to end this without saying that trust in God was something I always thought I had, and now I know I have it.

JANUARY 4, 1991

My recent days have had a new and different focus—my Martha, her surgery, her healing and recuperation, cooking, shopping, doing the washing, maintaining our house, relating to, and in a way, protecting her from the avalanche of love, caring, and concern from family, friends, and acquaintances. My preoccupation with Martha has been total, consuming each day of the last five weeks.

To focus on someone other than myself and my disease is energizing. We've often heard speculations about people *willing* themselves to diminish their own physical problems—even to forestall what seemed to be imminent death—because of the need to attend to the pressing needs of another. I believe it. I don't doubt it for a minute. During these weeks of Martha's need and dependence, my own symptoms and continuing problems have been reduced to all but nothing.

This has been a wondrous experience for Martha and me. In a way we have switched roles. For so long, Martha has been the watcher and I the watchee. But in recent weeks, we have been able to know the stress and pain of the other role, and we are sure that switching roles has done us good and will serve us well as the future unfolds.

While Martha came through her surgery with almost entirely positive results, there was great risk, and the potential for her death was clearly a reality. So we feel as if we have been to the mountain and have seen so much. Our belief and faith has turned to knowledge. We know there is healing, restoration, a gift from God. We know that even in darkness there is light. We know that strength and courage are there for the asking. We know that no matter what happens to us in the future, it is OK.

As the New Year came, we rejoiced that we have each other, alive and whole. We know more than ever before the beauty of each day—and in particular are grateful to have that day together.

JANUARY 6, 1991

It happened again. For no reason known to me, I fell. This time I cracked my head and opened a gash behind my left ear. It appears I lost consciousness, but I don't know whether that occurred before or after I fell.

Surely I'll want an evaluation of all this, and this episode brings into focus a fact that has bothered me for several years. My principal physicians are split between two hospitals, Bob at Riverside and Stan at University, which is now the location for the new cancer hospital. Bob refers to physicians who practice at Riverside; Stan sends his referrals to those at University. Before this becomes an issue and I find myself a patient at Riverside without access to Stan, it seems appropriate to find a new

internist who practices at University. So I've begun the process—
reluctantly but with confidence it's the right thing to do.

FEBRUARY 2, 1991

Chuck heard from Stan. The results of his PSA came back at 6.2.
Needless to say, this caught our attention. It's a big jump—from 3.9 to
6.2 in four months.

FEBRUARY 3, 1991

Last night was different. It was as if a new chapter had opened.
I slept fitfully, wakened frequently. I wasn't stressed, but I was
anxious. I was adjusting, getting my head screwed on again, and
dealing with the implications of yesterday's news.

FEBRUARY 7, 1991

As we anticipated, Stan is reluctant to begin any new treatment
because there is nothing to do to slow down the progression—
only to offer palliation. He simply seeks good days, and these
are such.

     With this knowledge, Martha and I decided to get down and
dirty—to ask some direct, specific questions. We knew that
these questions would put him on the spot and that we were
seeking information he might not wish to discuss. "For pur-
poses of planning our lives, Stan," we asked, "how many more
good days might we anticipate?" He said it was impossible for
him to know with certainty, but because he was aware of our
zest for life and for living together to the fullest, he would discuss probabilities. He told me to expect six to twelve months
of good days, and after that it would be downhill.

     We told him we had read material on "androgen deprivation
escape"—the point at which the hormonal treatment is ineffec-
tive. "When does escape occur, Stan?" I asked. "When does the
meter start running, because what we've read comments that
death usually follows escape within six months."

     "You have already experienced escape," he answered, "but
really what you are talking about is the point at which your
PSA is perhaps 60, your energy level markedly reduced, and
your bone scan reveals considerable additional metastasis."

     Then the big question. "How long will I live?" Of course he
equivocated. He said he would be delighted if it were thirty-six

months, and he didn't discard this as a possibility. But he kept making references to twenty months, and I'm sure that was the best he could do and also more than he wanted to say.

> Stan was so good and patient as we questioned him (I should say as Chuck questioned him—but I was listening closely). I'm glad Chuck has read so much on his disease and has shared it with me, even when it has been hard to hear, and I just wanted the whole thing to go away. Chuck asked him what timetable he saw, and Stan answered that no one can tell. He did say, however, that since Chuck and I like to travel and do things, we should do them in the next six to twelve months. That's a BIG statement, even when the doctor says he'll be glad to be wrong. Stan is always forthright with us and we're glad for that. It does make it easier for us.
>
> What did it do to me? I was devastated to discover the time is upon us. I know we have good days ahead of us, but I also know each good day makes for one fewer. I am apprehensive, because I don't want Chuck to hurt. I am scared. I don't want to be alone. And I hurt! I am brittle as I deal with where we are and what's ahead. I know that strength and courage are there for both of us. If I didn't believe that, I can't imagine how I would feel.

It was a big day. We didn't sleep well last night. We had a lot to think about, and today we talked and talked, our conversation punctuated by the flow of cleansing and restoring tears. Gosh, our plate is full. We've been through a lot, particularly during these last ninety days. It just doesn't seem necessary to experience this progression of my disease directly on the heels of Martha's surgery and recuperation.

Death has now become a reality, no longer an abstraction. Now we wonder. We hear a reference on TV to something being scheduled for 1993, and we wonder if I'll be here. We think about next Christmas and wonder what kind of shape I'll be in. I find myself counting out twenty months and visualizing October 1992.

For several years, Martha and I have been accumulating a fiftieth-anniversary fund to finance a family celebration. But that is three years away, and we wonder if it might be more appropriate to abandon the reference to the fiftieth anniversary and simply get the family together for fun and frolic at an earlier date.

FEBRUARY 19, 1991

Last night I had a dream that wakened me and caused me to consider its meaning at this moment in my life. The dream began in a classroom where I, with others, was a student. I don't recall the subject matter, but I do remember it was very interesting to me. I participated in a lively discussion that extended beyond the classroom to another setting.

The professor was a pleasant sort of man. I noted he was attractive and clean-cut. My impression was that he participated little in the discussions, although I was aware of his presence. The class broke up, and the professor and I were left alone together. We talked a little about the class, and as we talked, I noticed he was moving close to me. I was terribly uneasy, but he continued his approach and tried to kiss me. I turned away; his lips touched my neck behind my ear. I shoved him away and left.

The scene now changed. I went to my office to clean out my desk and take some things home, as I was about to retire from the life insurance business. There was a certain urgency to the task, because Martha was waiting for me in the car. I heard someone quietly ascending the stairs. It was the professor, dressed as before in a business suit, but this time wearing the hat of a naval officer. He again made physical advances on me. I struggled to resist him. I tried to fight him off, to no avail. My attempts to strike him with my clenched first were impotent; by the time my fist reached his face it was like a cream puff. My fist had no power. I tried to knee him in the groin with the same results. I was helpless.

At that point I awakened, startled and distressed, and I asked myself how I felt. I concluded I felt totally helpless and vulnerable—defenseless. I wondered about the meaning of the military hat, and it seemed to me it signified the kind of authority one experiences in the military when required to obey the orders of a superior no matter what. These are surely the feelings I have about the progression of my cancer.

It was a powerful and memorable dream which I feel came from the depths of my being and confirmed my feelings as I move into an untidy future.

MARCH 1, 1991

I've been reluctant to seek a new internist, because Bob has been superb, and it gave Martha some stress that her doctor would no longer have an ongoing relationship with me and thus would be unable to talk with her professionally about me. Nonetheless, based on Bob's hospital affiliation, I felt I had to move ahead. I am now in the hands of Dr. Cindi, and even at this early date we have enormous confidence in her.

We spent a couple of hours with her last week, giving her the opportunity to get acquainted with me and my history. She seems to be focusing initially on my falling and my increasing leg weakness, her attention being directed to the possibility the metastatic sites may be pressing on nerves that affect my legs. She wanted to see the results of an MRI of the pelvic area, but that was ruled out because of the metal parts of my penile prosthesis, so she has to fall back on a CT scan.

I've had only one major fall in recent weeks, but another minor spill occurred yesterday. When I was getting out of my chair, my left leg failed to hold and I went down. It was the first time my left leg has given way; the fact it had previously been my right leg didn't escape Cindi's notice. It seems a strange contradiction, at least to me, that Martha and I walk three or four miles every day at a fairly vigorous pace, yet I have this growing sense of weakness in my legs. I have always had a certain amount of trouble with balance, but now it has become a problem. As I walk I stumble easily, scuff my feet, and resist climbing stairs or stepping up curbs. All this distresses me, but I feel helpless to do anything about it. Some days my feelings of weakness are more pronounced, and on those days I have an increased sense of insecurity and uncertainty. We are hoping Dr. Cindi can get to the bottom of this and offer some solutions.

MARCH 5, 1991

Today I had my CT scan. Because he cares (as does his wife, Ann), Bud Sapp, our close friend, called and asked us to allow him to drive us over to the hospital, to wait for us there, and to bring us home. It was hard for me to accept this offer (I am perfectly capable of driving over myself) but I knew he needed to express himself in this way.

What a loving person Bud is. I have prayed to God to teach
me to be a channel of His love. My prayers have been answered
more times than I can count. I'm learning.

MARCH 6, 1991

Martha asked me how I felt about yesterday's CT scan. My
answer was that I was at peace. She understood that from her
own experience of being at peace prior to her brain surgery. It
wasn't the scan about which I felt peaceful; it was the whole
experience of having and dealing with my disease.

MARCH 28, 1991

On our way to Florida, I finished Jean Craig's *Between Hello and
Goodbye* and have been trying to analyze my feelings. It is the story
of how a couple struggled and lived with the husband's lung cancer
until he died. There were times when I admired his wanting to take
charge of his own body, but to my way of thinking, it was selfishly
done. He asked his family not to tell others of his illness, which
denied them the support they needed, and his wife felt so alone. He
also carried on as if it were business as usual, buying another company that needed his attention and would require the whole family's
attention to make it survive after his death. It's true the family did
take over, but at a price to them. Jean was a devoted wife, but devoted to the extent she wouldn't disagree with him, to her own detri-
ment. She gave and gave and hurt and hurt.

Normalcy is what everyone desires, and everyone seeks it in his
or her own way. In Jean's book, it seems that fighting and struggling
and trying to ignore the disease are the paths to normalcy. I also had
the feeling Jean and her husband were doing this alone, without the
support of God, Christ, or the Holy Spirit, and that has to be a lone-
ly existence.

People have different ways of coping, but I'm so glad we look cancer straight in the eye. It isn't a pretty picture, and I wish with all my
heart it would go away, but by looking squarely at the situation,
Chuck and I can talk about it, cry about it, live with it, and even laugh
about some aspects of it. It doesn't dominate us, because we aren't
fighting it. We aren't giving in, but we accept it and get on with our
lives, enjoying each day to the fullest.

Some days are easier than others, that's true, but we know everything possible is being done for Chuck, so we're not mad at anyone.
Our feeling is one of helplessness, not anger. We also have the sup-

port of great faith, a faith that never leaves and is proven, even in darkness.

I'm glad I read the book, but I'm glad we don't cope that way.

Sitting by the pool, Martha said, "It must frustrate and disappoint you to keep having the weakness in your legs even after so much restful living." Frustration? Disappointment? She chooses her words well. She was right on target. My first reaction was to deny those feelings, but the more I pondered her question, the more I knew those are my feelings. But what about a whole bunch of other words that might express one's feelings? Bitterness? Resentment? Fear? Anger? Despair? Discouragement? Dejection? Regret? None of them. Not a whit.

Acceptance is essential, of both the big issues and the small nuances and day-to-day changes that occur, but equally important is one's expectation of what death and eternal life are all about. If one's expectation or fear is that at death, one drops off into a dismal, dark abyss—into eternal silence and nothingness—if one simply goes "Poof!" then one might expect to feel bitterness, resentment, fear, and anger as one observes the gradual slipping I'm going through. But I don't feel that way, and although I may be deluding myself, I don't ever expect to. I believe acceptance, coupled with the expectation of death as an exciting adventure, opens me to know and experience God's peace.

Time will tell, of course, but I expect God's peace will support me all my days, even into what may well be terminal pain. It wouldn't surprise me in the least to experience a relatively painless journey to and into the end. God's peace is one element of God's grace which together with His love, acceptance, forgiveness and healing, is showered on all people regardless of their deserving. The gifts are blocked only by our bitterness, resentment, fear, anger, despair, discouragement, dejection, or regret.

APRIL 2, 1991

People are prone to ask Martha, "How is Chuck doing?" She answers them and often says, "Why don't you ask Chuck? He'll be happy to tell you." They seldom do, though, nor do most people want to receive much detail. And rarely does anyone ask Martha how she's doing.

In Sun City, Florida, I visited a neighbor of our friend Marilyn who was operated on two weeks ago for prostate cancer. He's still strung up to his catheter and facing four to six weeks of radiation, as his is a Stage C. (It has metastasized to the seminal vesicles.) He's not ready to talk about the road ahead, so we talked mostly about his current status and ways of dealing with his approaching incontinence. Talking with him was good for me—not only to be able to share with him, but also to be aware of a renewed sense of gratitude about the five years we've had since we were where he is now.

APRIL 1, 1991

Even with our peace, we have moments of misunderstanding. Fortunately, we talk, think, and pray about those moments. One occurred last evening when I felt from the expression on Chuck's face that he was "lowering the blinds" on me while I talked of my hurt. This made me feel very alone. Last night as I meditated and prayed, I realized he wasn't lowering the blinds; the look on his face and in his eyes was helplessness. He's helpless to do anything about the cancer or my hurt. How blind I was! We are used to traveling the same road, but this time there is a fork in the road, where Chuck will go one way and I another. Even as we travel now, it's as though we are on different, side-by-side paths.

How can I help her? She hurts, and she says she feels as if we are going separate ways in this totally existential experience. She illustrates this by touching her hands together just below the wrists and forming a V. We feel and hurt for each other, but neither of us has died before or experienced watching a lover slip away. It isn't grim really, but it is intense.

APRIL 17, 1991

PSA is 8.6, drifting up again. No further treatment yet, although Stan says it's OK to increase the Voltaren to 150 mg per day as needed. I asked him about removing the penile implant to permit MRI. He doesn't want to do it; he says there's no sense in running the risk of infection, and he's perfectly happy to use CT scans. He chided me a little for getting too technical.

MAY 6, 1991

Three cheers for Voltaren! The increased dose is working wonders. I still have some pain, but it hasn't been necessary to supplement with Tylenol. I wonder, however, what level of pain I might be experiencing with no medication at all. The pharmacist says that 150 mg per day is the maximum recommended dosage. Little by little, change is manifest, and it's always downhill. I've always said a hill has two sides, but I guess this is the exception.

MAY 7, 1991

Today as I stood in the kitchen baking, the tears flowed over my cheeks. I just let them flow, as I continued measuring ingredients. An amazing thing happened. When the tears stopped, the knots in my stomach were gone. As I was crying, unable to stop, I remembered others telling me that Chuck had been that way the day of my surgery, because he felt so threatened and apprehensive about the future. That memory helped me understand how threatened I am by Chuck's illness.

I feel so helpless in the face of the cancer, but it's been a good day in spite of my struggles. Struggles have again helped me get my feet back on the ground and to have faith in the future. I can feel God's peace. God's peace has such a difficult time getting through when I block its passage. Thank heaven, God is patient.

MAY 8, 1991

I knew it would happen sooner or later. Others have observed that cancer patients invariably get advice from others, sometimes from considerable distance away, about miraculous benefits to unknown patients who have tried this or that. Our dear friends in Denver have a son who is a young oncologist in Seattle. Through his mother, he sent me word of an experimental program at the University of Washington that is offering prostate cancer patients great relief from pain. He urged his mother to urge me to urge my urologist to contact the professionals in charge of the program to seek my participation in it. Interestingly, these friends will be visiting next week, and I know they'll want to know what I've done about their suggestion. I'll simply have to thank them and gently advise them that:

- My pain is not sufficiently intense to warrant my submitting to anything greater than I'm taking now.
- I'm reluctant to second-guess Stan and put him in the position of having to respond to this suggestion. I am completely confident in Stan and want to depend on him for treatment options, and I also want to avoid being caught between competing protocols.
- I'm reluctant to participate in any treatment administered or controlled from twenty-five hundred miles away.

When I was first diagnosed, a friend sent me a copy of a flier touting a drug available in Canada but not in the United States. And I recall my friend, George, who refused the recommendations of the urologists of the Cleveland Clinic, returning there only in the waning days of his life.

Thank you, I'll stick with Stan.

JUNE 1, 1991

It's been six months since my surgery—a fascinating six months. The process of coming back to normal has been fast in some ways, slow in others, and frustrating at times.

About two weeks after the surgery, the muscles on the right side of my face seemed to be paralyzed. It is the responsibility of everyone who works at the Village to report anything that seems amiss with a resident, and so it was the cleaning lady who noticed my face and reported it to the clinic. They sent a nurse down. When she saw me, she asked if she could call my doctor. We all felt better on hearing that what I was experiencing was to be expected. I was frustrated, however, and worked hard to get my face to respond. Within a few weeks, it did.

When one side of my face was sluggish, it was hard to eat; the muscles and tongue wouldn't move the food for me to swallow. For many weeks I chewed only on the left side. Brushing my teeth was another problem, as my gums were numb and I couldn't feel anything on the right side. I had to make a special effort to brush those teeth. Today it's much better. The numbness around my mouth is so minimal that the act of putting on lipstick is no longer a challenge—and it certainly was a challenge when I couldn't feel anything. The only time the right side of my mouth stiffens now is when I'm tired, and only Chuck and I are aware of it.

My right eye was traumatized, so it blinked more slowly than the left. Chuck said my eyes worked like venetian blinds, which must have been funny to watch. I called my right eye my Deadeye Dick eye, because there was no expression in it for a while. I saw double vertically until prisms were put into my glasses in March. What a joy that was! I hadn't been able to read until then. Thank goodness for Chuck's reading to me and for taped books. Until the prisms, I hadn't been able to drive either, so when I got them, I felt as if I was finally getting back to normal.

It is a great experience to touch the right side of my forehead, my face, and my nose. There is so much we take for granted until we no longer have it. I rejoice as I blink, as I feel the right side of my tongue, as I eat without food falling out of my mouth. I rejoice to swallow, to see wrinkles in the right side of my face, to smile, to feel tears in my eyes. I rejoice even as I feel the dent in the back of my head, because it symbolizes Dr. Hal's skill, and for that I thank God.

I'm feeling more like myself every day and realize how fortunate I am. Physical adjustments always come with surgery, but I wasn't prepared for the psychological adjustments I had to make. I knew the numbness in my face and my Deadeye Dick eye were to be expected, but I was fearful people would think I was "different." Along with the problems of my face and eye came the loss of hearing in my right ear and some imbalance, all of which made me very insecure. Chuck's wonderful encouragement and love, combined with the improvement in my facial nerves, have solved the psychological difficulties.

Five percent of the tumor was left because it involved the brain stem, and cutting it away could have caused many more problems. Hal used the laser to stop the blood supply to the tumor and, we hope, slow down any growth. The doctors feel the original tumor had been growing for seven years or more. I had an MRI after the surgery to determine the size of the remaining tumor and will have another MRI this fall to see if it's growing.

There is a possibility I might have to have this operation again in ten years, but no one knows for sure. It may be that if tumor growth wasn't halted with the laser, it was slowed down enough not to bother me again. It doesn't worry me, because I know I'm in good hands, and if I have to have it done again, I will.

JUNE 2, 1991

I'm aware Chuck is losing his battle as I watch him will his legs to work when we're walking and I notice his fatigue. I'm aware of his determination to do everything he wants to; his spirit is indomitable. I try not to be overprotective, but it's hard since I want him to save his strength and energy. He replies that it's not reserving energy that's important; it's going and doing while he has the strength, because the day will come when that energy won't be there.

Chuck knows better than anyone how his body feels, so I take my cues from him as to what he can do. One thing I've learned is that each day must stand on its own. We take each day for what it brings. There are days that are good and others that aren't as good as we'd like. When we have a day that's not good, it's important not to judge the coming days by that one.

I'm anxious over the future, and I know it's because Chuck's illness might upset anything we plan. We've been fortunate in always planning ahead for vacations and family get-togethers. Now we aren't sure about plans. We are planning a trip to Jamaica with our kids and grandkids in August and planning to drive East in September. As Chuck's fatigue and weakness increase, he's not sure how he'll take ten days of constant living with family in Jamaica. I've tried to say that we'll have space, as the kids will be swimming, playing tennis, and so on. It's natural for him to feel nervous; he doesn't want others to be uncomfortable or to feel they have to tiptoe around.

Chuck is unsure about going East. He wonders if he'll be having medical treatment if his PSA has risen, so he says maybe we'll go in October. It makes no difference to me, but it makes me sad to see Chuck feeling so hesitant. To me it says his body is telling him that all is not well.

In the beginning of these journals, it was Chuck who wondered how much he would share with me. Now, since it helps me cope, I'm putting my feelings in writing. I don't want to sound negative, and I wonder how it will affect Chuck to know I'm apprehensive and frightened. I didn't know what I was going to write today; I only knew I needed to write so that I could discover what was bubbling around inside me.

I awaken each morning and look at the large framed poster on the wall of our bedroom. It depicts a little boy and girl holding hands, and the caption reads, "I love being us together." Martha and I purchased that poster in Boston. The caption caught the essence of our relationship and has expressed it ever since.

There it hangs, and I know one day it will bring Martha great pain—when being together will be but a memory. I have no idea what she'll do with the poster then, but I'll bet she thinks about it now, as I do.

JUNE 5, 1991

Five years ago today, they told me I had a 50-to-70 percent chance of five-year survival. Hallelujah!

JUNE 10, 1991

Since the fall of 1989, I've maintained a lively correspondence with twelve-year-old Aaron Reed, resulting from a pen pal program between some of us at the Village and a local school. In a recent letter, I revealed to him that I have cancer. I didn't want him to be surprised and to have a broken relationship without some prior knowledge. I said, "Aaron, you are my friend, and I want you to know something. For the past five years, I have had cancer and have been very fortunate it was discovered early and has been held at bay. It is slowly catching up with me. But these are still good days, and we hope they will continue through 1991."

What I didn't know when I wrote this was that Aaron's mother is employed by a pain-control program that operates out of the Riverside Hospice. In conversation with a public relations person at Riverside, she revealed Aaron's relationship with me. The PR person wrote a letter to a friend of hers at the *Columbus Dispatch*, suggesting this might make a story. Last week, the reporter, Mary Bridgeman, interviewed me, as she had interviewed Aaron, his mother, and his teacher. She also sent a photographer. Mary is a very skillful interviewer, asking penetrating questions and even more penetrating follow-up questions. She got down deep into my feelings—where I live. She asked:

- In telling Aaron of my cancer, was I attempting to set up a successor-mentor relationship?
- How does it feel to be a mentor?
- Why had I entered into this mentor relationship with Aaron?
- Why did I think my pen pal relationship with Aaron is the only one that has continued and flourished in the two years of this program?
- Can one really ever give himself away?

I felt exposed and vulnerable talking at this level with a reporter I had only just met. I said, "Mary, we have been open with all of our friends about my cancer. We have been free with our discussion, but it never occurred to me it might someday be spread out for public view in the press."

She was very sensitive and offered not to mention cancer in the article and then said, "But if you are willing to risk and will trust me, you might be of enormous help to someone."

I knew she was manipulating me with a powerful idea, and I understood. How many times had I done the same thing selling life insurance? I was silent, then turned to her and said, "OK, let's go." She thanked me and went on with her questioning.

The article is scheduled to appear next Sunday—Father's Day. I do feel vulnerable, but I hope she will be able to write it in a way that will, indeed, be encouraging, reassuring, and helpful to others. Years ago, I wrote and frequently delivered a speech called "It's the Ripples That Count." I believe it.

JUNE 11, 1991

People tell me I look great, and I thank them. And when I go to the cancer hospital, I look around at other patients, knowing they have cancer or they wouldn't be here, and nearly all of them look great, too. The other evening we met a lady we haven't seen for a long time, who we know is suffering from esophageal cancer, is being tube-fed, and is on heavy pain medication—and she looked wonderful. It's a crazy disease. Wondering how I *really* look, I asked Martha, and she told me I often look as if the cancer is wearing on me—I look tired. Later she told me she felt guilty for answering my query so directly and specifically.

We do try to protect one another, but we are experiencing this disease from different perspectives and we need to share them with each other. Martha often talks about our both being "uptight." We get stressed at different times and by different stimuli. We are traveling different parallel roads—within sight of one another but with different destinations.

I find it hard to acknowledge stress. As a matter of fact, I suspect this is the first time I have really faced up to it and admitted it. Martha attributes this to my take-charge personality. I think that way down deep I equate being in charge with being stress-free. To state it the opposite way, when I'm stressed I don't feel in charge.

JULY 3, 1991

What I have carefully referred to as discomfort is now pain. It has been increasing in the past few weeks, to the point where it overrides the pain medication I am taking at maximum dosage and supplementing with Tylenol. It is not disabling, but its presence is constant.

There are still good days, but we have to live defensively. Last week I had three or four really good days, and then the bottom fell out.

JULY 16, 1991

It seems to me that Chuck has been very eager to share his thoughts, his beliefs, and his philosophies, and that his emotions are terribly close to the surface. I welcome his being open to others but somehow it has threatened me because he is so eager. It's almost as though he wants to cram in as much as possible in the time he has left. That's threatening to me, as it makes me believe he doesn't think he's doing well. When I connect that feeling with his increasing weakness and fatigue, it's overwhelming to me.

I remarked about all this when Karen and her family were here. As we chatted, I realized Chuck's behavior really wasn't anything new. He has always enjoyed sharing his philosophy with others. I recalled all the speeches he has made and how I loved to hear him speak. When we were between churches, we didn't have much opportunity to share deep feelings with others who were also searching. Then we joined St. Mark's and began to make new friends, and as that happened, we began to trust "throwing out our pearls." It didn't bother me until this month when Chuck gave his "I Believe" talk. His eagerness to tell others his innermost thoughts was evident. My anxiety grew each time I heard him share those precious thoughts; it really undid me. Then out of the blue (don't tell me the Holy Spirit isn't real), I understood that his openness has always been there. It has just resurfaced in the five years we've been at St. Mark's, which happens to coincide with his cancer journey. Now it all makes sense to me.

JULY 17, 1991

We are holding our own. We saw Stan today and were both happily surprised to learn my PSA is only slightly more elevated, now standing at 9.

My increasing weakness and fatigue are, he suspects, due to

the involvement of nerves in my back. He seemed to indicate
it wasn't unusual. As to chemotherapy, he says he'll wait until
I tell him that my pain is not manageable with Voltaren and
Tylenol with codeine and that the fatigue is more than mildly
limiting.

JULY 18, 1991

We talk about good days and rejoice in each one, but perhaps
the standards by which we've judged good days are too strin-
gent, our expectations too great. So Martha and I have concluded that a good day is any day my pain can be managed with
my present medications and/or any day on which my fatigue
does not severely curtail my schedule. In a way it's like allowing
that something less than an A+ can qualify as a good grade. A
lowered definition allows us to accurately describe a day as
good, even a day on which I experience pain and weakness.

AUGUST 3, 1991

A lot of bread cast on the waters during my life has been coming back to me in recent days. When the article about Aaron
Reed appeared in the paper, the response was immediate—letters, notes, clippings, and remarks, and even an invitation for
Aaron and me to talk to a group of leaders from area high
schools.

Among the many nice things that were said were two I will
always cherish. The first came from a high school classmate
from fifty years ago. Betty Rehn Karch, with whom I performed
in operettas and in the senior class play, wrote from California
expressing her gratitude for "all the nice years" we had together, and she told me about visiting her sister, who was dying of
a brain tumor. She said:

"In June, Lloyd and I visited her in Michigan and had a wonderful and inspiring five days. Jane had always taught us how
to live, but now she was showing us how to die. She had no
regrets, had done the very best she could, and thought seventy-
one years was just fine. She seemed excited and grateful to have
lived to see her three children in their careers, all successful,
and she had gotten to enjoy her four grandchildren."

When I read those words, I was dissolved in tears. No one
has ever expressed better or more precisely how I feel.

The second expression came from Martha, who, with tears streaming down her face, told me of her joy at seeing my bread come back to me to be savored by me, rather than her hearing these sentiments after I'm gone. What an experience for both of us!

AUGUST 18, 1991

We have been in Jamaica for ten days of pure joy with our family—an accelerated fiftieth anniversary celebration. Perhaps I'll still be here in 1993, but it seems improbable, so we brought together the whole gang two years early without referring to the anniversary. Tonight Martha and I will announce Phase II of this gathering to be held on or about November 21, 1993, at which time the entire family will be our guests for dinner at a Columbus White Castle [a local fast-food restaurant].

Martha and I are in hog heaven. We have never been more happy. While I have lived defensively, avoiding using all my energy reserves, we have experienced a strange sense of detachment about my illness—almost as if it weren't a reality. Martha says it would be great if we could maintain this detachment at home.

AUGUST 25, 1991

We convened our family, all eight of them, for ten glorious days. Several years ago, Chuck and I had started saving one hundred dollars here and fifty dollars there to make it possible for us to gather our family in some special place for our fiftieth. Stan had encouraged us to do any special traveling this year while Chuck had the strength, so we decided to move the trip up. It was billed as a celebration of almost forty-eight years of marriage, and what better way to celebrate love and life together than with the fruits of that marriage?

Tom and Carol had been to Jamaica several times and felt this was the ideal place to go—and it was. We had two condos, one sleeping four, the other six, close to one another. A cook and two maids were furnished, so none of us had to cook or do laundry or housework. One could easily get spoiled. Karen, Carol, and I did the marketing and planning of meals, and it was fun to shop in the open-air markets. Even with the bargaining we learned to do, the maids would tell us we had paid too much or the fruit wasn't good. Oh, well.

During the day, everyone did what he or she wanted. The ocean and pool were outside our window, tennis courts were available, and there was sightseeing to be done. Chuck and I took in some of the sights, but for the most part, he conserved his energy. It was wonderful to see him sitting on our porch overlooking the Caribbean, as he whittled or drank coffee and talked to the maids or family members.

One afternoon everyone left while I remained behind on the porch. Said Martha to Pansy, one of the maids, "Take good care of Chuck." Later Tom joined me on the porch and Pansy, wanting to go to the store, said, "Tom, I need to go out. Can you take care of old grandfather while I am gone?" Trusting that all this characterization represented was a failure of conversational nuance, everybody laughed.

Each day we all had happy hour at our condo at 6:00 p.m. and dinner at the other condo around 7:00. After we had all done what we wanted to do during the day (thus giving everyone time and space), we were eager to join together and share tales, both humorous and serious. One evening we all sat on the porch overlooking the water and sang. That was such fun! The entire time was nothing but joy for all of us.

One thing that was wonderful to observe was the bonding of the cousins, Brian, Colby, and Nicole. Eighteen-, sixteen-, and fourteen-year-olds have a lot to share, and it was great to see it happen. Little Max, who will be four in October, didn't take part in the bonding, but he did his part with the rest of us in the pool. Oh, how he loved the water!

There was not one note of sadness on this trip, even though everyone knew it had been advanced in time. No one felt anything but joy and gratitude.

AUGUST 29, 1991

My defensive living paid off in Jamaica, but by the time we arrived back in Columbus, I was a basket case.

We rose at 5:15 a.m. on the day of departure from Jamaica, sharing a van for the sixty-mile trip to get Karen, Doug, Brian, and Colby to Montego Bay for an early flight. The trip was hard, bouncing around as we did on a miserable road, bumpy and curvy. Thank goodness for the small pillow at my back. After depositing the Smiths, Karen's family, at the airport, we drove on another 45 minutes each way to a place where Tom and Carol wanted to purchase some woodcarvings. The road was no better, but I was doing fairly well. We shopped some more in Montego Bay and then went on to the airport for our own flights.

We had nearly a two-hour wait, so we made our way to an air-conditioned restaurant to bide our time. The restaurant was on the second floor and was reached by a flight of twelve to fifteen steps. As I climbed, my legs became weaker and weaker, and by the time I arrived at the top step, I simply lacked the strength to negotiate it. Down I went. Fortunately, I suffered no more injury than a slice on my left arm, but I was shaken. A couple of cups of wonderful Jamaican coffee restored me.

The flight to Newark, where we spent the night, was eventless, but it was after 9:00 p.m. when we finally made it to the motel. The next morning we went to the airport a couple of hours before our flight, and bad weather delayed our departure for four hours beyond the scheduled time. The terminal was frigid, and when we boarded the plane, the flight attendant was kind enough to bring blankets, which felt mighty good. It was well into the evening before we finally got home, tired and hungry. Since then, I've been attempting to get back some strength and energy. Both are so limited.

We are piling it in while the days are good; yet we are trying to do so with reason and restraint. We leave next week for ten days in the East. It has been more than a year since we visited the kids in their homes, and we want to do that. It seems wise to do it now.

SEPTEMBER 2, 1991

It's Labor Day. We think back to Labor Day 1990, when we were wondering what Labor Day 1991 would bring, and now here we are, somewhat less energetic and more weak, but we are here, and that is encouraging. If my deterioration progresses as slowly as it seems to be now, I may be around for the dawn of the new century. Who knows?

The day has been contemplative and sad in another way. For many months I've been whittling the figures of a little boy and girl for Martha. In recent weeks the carving has sat on my table nearly finished. But something in me was reluctant to complete it. Today I finished it, and it sort of did me in. There was something so final about it. The creation of these little figures was all over. Hours and hours of work. A few cut or punctured fingers. Lots of love in every stroke of my knives.

What now? I've been working on some nameplates for our grandchildren. I've made a little potbellied man for Karen and a car for Tom. It seems as if anything I whittle hereafter will be superfluous.

The real work I set out to do is done.

SEPTEMBER 23, 1991

While I do try to practice moderation in my activities, I am reluctant to give up doing those things that may cause difficulty. Yesterday I served the chalice at communion, and the pain from bending over became so intense I leaned against the altar table, perspiration rolling off my brow. I regret the scene it must have created; it was enough that another participant asked if I was all right, and Martha, also serving, saw my distress and ashen face. This was an unusually intense episode, but even so, I am unwilling to give up serving yet. Concessions have been made—oh, so gradually—but one after another, each is a concession to cancer, never once a restoration of what once was.

The good news is that Martha received a superior report from her neurosurgeon. Her residual effects are improving, and the MRI showed no growth in the portion of the tumor that had to be left behind.

SEPTEMBER 29, 1991

I haven't written since Jamaica, and much has happened since then. The time has been filled with good days. Ten of those days found us visiting Tom and family and Karen and family in Washington and Boston, respectively. How wonderful it was to know we were welcome, even though we had recently spent ten days together. There's something special about visiting your kids in their homes and on their turf, about watching how their days are filled. It's a little peek into their lives.

I was pleased at how well Chuck felt the entire time. Driving four hundred miles on back-to-back days didn't give him more pain. He did have a difficult time the day we arrived in Washington, as the pain in his back simply would not disappear, and it was easy to see he was hurting. The week before we left for the trip had been packed with activity, and Chuck had been unable to get all the sleep he needed, so he really started this trip from behind.

Fortunately the following day and subsequent days found him feeling well, with little pain. While we were at Tom's, we were able to relax during the day, as everyone was at work or school, and we had the house to ourselves. Tom and the family were very careful not to plan anything that would keep us up late or drain Chuck's energy. Chuck left Tom's feeling rested, and that was so helpful. It was a great visit, with time to sit on the patio and talk, to walk to Tom's office and have lunch with him, and to share with Carol, Nicole, and little Max.

Our time with Karen was also planned with Chuck in mind. Our kids are so thoughtful! Since we were planning to attend one of Colby's soccer games, Karen made arrangements to take Chuck to the playing field, to find out where it would be most comfortable for him to sit, as bleacher seats aren't quite the choice for his back. Karen also talked with the athletic director and received permission to drive onto the field and park close, so Chuck wouldn't have far to walk. Although all this special attention was hard for Chuck to receive, he realized that what she had done was making it possible for him to see Colby play, and that the love she has for her dad was all that mattered. There were tears of love and gratitude in all our eyes.

Our whole stay with Karen was filled with talks, walks, and hugs. As at Tom's, the thoughtfulness over Chuck's energy level made it possible for us to leave for home rested and full of love.

SEPTEMBER 30, 1991

It all seems so incongruous. I love life so much. I cherish each day, and I have absolutely no wish to leave, but on the other hand I find myself praying that when the good days are over I go out fast, without lingering. Once the die is cast, I wish minimum hurt for my family. This is my prayer.

We have been dealing with concessions for quite some time. They have come so gradually, I'm not sure when they really started. I do know we've been pacing ourselves for perhaps two years; my brain surgery accelerated the need to do so.

I mentioned that before we left for the East, we had been very busy. In addition to the busyness, Chuck was having pain that wouldn't respond to the Voltaren and Tylenol. His internist recommended Tylenol with codeine. Chuck wanted to have it for the trip, as he didn't want to have pain he couldn't control when we were out of town.

Rationally, I wanted him to have the prescription, but emotionally I didn't want to think he needed codeine. I've taken Tylenol 3 and know it's OK (Tylenol comes in numbers 1, 2, 3, and 4, each doubling the amount of codeine), but when I've taken it, I've known that in time the pain would go away. In Chuck's case, it meant the cancer was gaining on him. I didn't like to feel we were approaching the point where something more drastic would have to be done to manage pain. I know he's a long way from that point, but it's creeping up and I can't stop it.

I want to do everything in my power to keep Chuck from getting tired or hurting. I love to have him with me in the kitchen–it is our bliss–but I don't want to do anything that would add to his discomfort. I know I bother him when I nag him sometimes about picking up something heavy or when I try to protect him in other ways.

We had a talk yesterday about the Tylenol 3 question. He told me he wants to continue doing what he enjoys; he doesn't want to stop doing things that might bring him pain, because if he does, he'll just sit in his chair and do nothing, and that's not bliss. Even if by doing nothing he wouldn't have to take as much medication, it wouldn't be worth it. By taking the medicine, we can live the way we have always lived and the way he wants to continue living.

OCTOBER 6, 1991

Yesterday was a truly great day. Tom, Carol, Nicole, and Max were here for the weekend, but the purpose of the visit was our annual day at an Ohio State (OSU) game, as Tom's guest. The girls and kids went off shopping while Tom and I first attended the university president's pregame luncheon and then the game, made all the more enjoyable by an OSU victory over Wisconsin. It was great togetherness in spite of the plunging temperature during the game. Bless his heart, Tom went out during the third quarter to buy me a sweat shirt, but there were none to be found; there had been a total sell-out. I was uncomfortable but determined to stay even if I turned into an icicle, the only threat of that being in my imagination.

There was one vivid revelation to me in all of this. I remember the discomfort in my back as I sat in the B-deck boxes last year. This year was even more uncomfortable in spite of the fact that I'd fortified myself with plenty of medication in self-defense. I also remember that last year, we parked a long, long way from the stadium, walking briskly to the horseshoe and ascending the ramps and stairs to B deck at the speed of the crowd. This year it was far different. Tom had arranged for stadium parking passes, but the trip up the stairs and ramp was far different. I clung to

the railings to assist the climb, and our speed was such that everyone passed us. Once in my seat, I remained seated during the
game, refraining from jumping up with the crowd. I missed some
exciting plays, but the old legs wouldn't serve me in such repeat-
ed getting on my feet. As we walked back to the car (actually my
gait was more of a weave and a stagger at times), I was increasingly grateful for those parking passes.

It was a wonderful day—pure joy—but a marked difference
from last year. I wondered what Tom was thinking, but I didn't
ask. No need to cast a pall over such a great afternoon with a
great guy.

OCTOBER 14, 1991

It's evident to both of us the pace of change is picking up. It
seems to have begun about a month ago when, for no apparent
reason, my back pain became acute and severe. The Voltaren
failed to manage it, and in the past week I have supplemented
with Tylenol and codeine. With Tylenol 3 as the supplement,
there is a noticeable improvement. But today, even with the
new combination of medicines, the pain was intense.

> When I went into the den, I found Chuck dealing with a painful back
> spasm that radiated clear around to his entire abdomen. He had been
> doing some kneading of the bread for me and had also ironed some
> handkerchiefs, so I immediately thought those two things were the
> culprits. But who knows?
>
> Chuck says if it's so, so be it. He's going to continue doing what he
> likes, and one of those things is kneading bread. After a while, the
> pain in his back settled down, but the tightness in my stomach con-
> tinues.

This pain is a marked change, and both Martha and I are mind-
ful of Stan's comment that he doesn't want to start chemotherapy until the pain overrides the Tylenol with codeine. It sure
overrode it today. My next date with Stan is November 13. We
wonder what will unfold in the next few weeks and what Stan's
decision will be.

OCTOBER 15, 1991

Chuck says that he went back two years in his journal and read how he felt at the time. He says there is no doubt the cancer is on the move, and he feels it.

This morning, as we walked, he told me he had something to say and he knew it would be hard on me. Tears were running down his face. He gave me the list of precious things he wants to present to Tom, Karen, Carol, Doug, Brian and Colby, Nicole and Max. Yes, it was hard for me to hear, and tears ran down my cheeks, too.

It's important he give these things to their new owners while he is still alive and can see the joy receiving them will bring to the children. I am sad when I think of *Boy,* a clay figure of a young boy, not sitting on the table or when I think of not seeing Chuck's cross around his neck, but it is important for Chuck to give *Boy* to Tom and to put his cross and gold chain around Karen's neck. He will seem undressed without the cross I gave him, but I agree Karen must have it.

On another day this week, Chuck talked with Nancy Billings, the director of residence services here at the Village, and before he hung up the phone, he asked her about the hospice. I was sitting in the den and nearly fell off the couch. It was a real shocker because we hadn't even talked about hospice ourselves. We had both thought about it, but we hadn't dealt with the issue directly.

I puddled up and was undone. We talked the matter up one side and down the other, and as always, I realized it was better to discuss the hospice before the services were needed and to begin to get the Village involved. I know that by talking in advance of need, there is time to rebound, pick up the pieces, and get on with enjoying each day.

NOVEMBER 1, 1991

Although we have been very fortunate in being able to continue our lifestyle, yesterday Chuck made a major concession, one that was hard for him to make, and it broke my heart. Both of us are chalice bearers at St. Mark's, and the experience of serving the chalice to others is most meaningful and significant. It is a privilege to do so. The last time Chuck served he was in such pain, my heart fell to my feet to watch him. Yesterday he had to say he could no longer serve.

The last time I served the chalice, I knew it would be my final time. (But how special it was to do it with Martha!) I will now have to limit my activities to those of a lector. I have conceded reluctantly and with deep sadness. This one was not easy for me.

NOVEMBER 6, 1991

Saw Stan today. Knowing how much I have deteriorated in the past sixty days, we were prepared for whatever his recommendation might be. We had supposed my PSA would be highly elevated and he would suggest chemo. We had hoped we could forestall that until after the first of the year and get past Thanksgiving and Christmas before having to deal with the toxicity Stan says is part of the process. However, he told us my PSA is 11.2, a rise of only two points since July. We were surprised and elated, but then Stan commented that the PSA is not totally reliable to mark the progress of the disease. He has known patients with PSAs of over 1000 who have no pain and others with readings as low as 4.9 who have severe pain. Now isn't that a kettle of fish?! The more we know the more we know how little we know.

Then we talked about chemotherapy. Stan kept shying away from it, although you could see him turning it over in his mind. He described the side effects, the hair loss, and the discomfort. He reminded us it is beneficial only as a palliative measure, and for the first time he advised us that even as a palliative it helps for only three to four months. It was increasingly clear he was opting for radiation, if feasible. A bone scan will show the number and location of tumors. If they are so numerous that zapping them is out of the question, radiation will give me relief from the pain associated with the most troublesome spots. So next week, after a bone scan, I'll have a consultation with a radiologist.

I asked Stan if I would be alive in another twelve months. He said he would not be surprised if I were, but neither would he be surprised if I were not.

We are clearly once again in a new phase. We are now facing a future marked by continued breakdown and complications that will have to be dealt with individually and symptomatically. It's almost as if we can anticipate the roof falling in sometime during the next year. Strangely, this is reassuring to me. I function better when I have the facts and possibilities laid out for me.

NOVEMBER 12, 1991

A year ago, we were waiting for my brain surgery, and here I am today, writing on my computer. My face has no paralysis whatsoever. I knew how lucky I was, but my good fortune was really underscored the other day by two events. The first was when Bob told me I had no paralysis because Hal had been so patient and had taken so much time. The twelve hours on the operating table really paid off. Next, we were seated beside a neurosurgeon at a dinner, and when he found out I'd had an acoustic neuroma, he said it was remarkable I had no paralysis. Wow!

The little bit of numbness around the right side of my mouth is nothing, and the tingling I get now and then means the nerves are still repairing themselves. That's good news. The deafness in my right ear really doesn't bother me unless I'm in a crowded or noisy room. Then it's difficult to ferret out what I'm wanting to hear. There are times, while listening to the radio or watching television or while someone across the room is saying something, when I miss important nuances. I try to fill in with what I think I missed, sometimes well, sometimes not too accurately. All this has made me aware of how necessary it is for me to listen with undivided attention. There's something about having two hearing ears that gives you two chances to catch what's being said.

This past weekend, Chuck and I attended the diocesan convention in Dayton. It was a challenge for me, as I was in a huge room with perhaps five hundred others. We were seated at tables of ten. The first day I was confused by everything that was going on and also by trying to hear my tablemates and/or to eliminate the noise emanating from the rest of the room. Even when we left to visit the exhibits, the cacophony was difficult. As the day wore on, I decided I'd just have to get what I could and forget the rest. I discovered the best thing for me to do is to enter into a one-to-one chat and let the general conversation go on without my participation.

The next day I learned how to sit at the table so as to hear what was going on without being overwhelmed by all the voices coming at me. And I learned not to get uptight when I couldn't hear something and not to be shy about asking people to repeat. When it was important for people to understand why I might not respond, I explained the situation. Communication was better all the way around.

It's been a fascinating year, and I'm happy that as far as my health is concerned, all is well. The good Lord, my skilled surgeon, and my wonderful Chuck and family, along with our church and friends, have made this a remarkable time of healing and love. Praise be to God.

NOVEMBER 17, 1991

Chuck had severe pain yesterday. He took the Percocet Stan had given him for when the Tylenol 4 (yes, he's on more codeine) didn't help.

Martha didn't feel as reassured as I did by our last meeting with Stan. She found it disturbing. For me it confirmed how I was feeling. To her it spelled the beginning of a downhill slide that will inevitably result in separation.

At our Monday silent time with Michael Jupin, she spilled—overflowed—in front of our associate rector, Melody Williams, and Ann Sapp. What a time to do it! The love and support were magnificent. They told her that it was OK to feel this way, that it will stand her in good stead to have acknowledged these feelings so far in advance. They loved her and accepted and understood, and guess what? Their response was reassuring to her. So while we are reassured by totally different things, we are both reassured.

Later on, Ann and Bud Sapp stopped by and brought us a single yellow rose. Beautiful!

DECEMBER 5, 1991

The bone scan revealed growth of the tumors giving me the most pain, as well as a number of other spots here and there not sufficiently mature to cause trouble. Blood work followed.

Dr. G., the radiation oncologist, confirmed Stan's belief that radiation to the two troublesome spots in my back would likely afford some pain relief and enable me to back off the pain medication. So I am well into a series of radiation treatments that are administered Monday through Friday for two weeks. The radiation staff cautions that there is no thought of cure, no expectation of greater longevity, only comfort, and they enumerate potential side effects such as nausea, increased fatigue, irritation of my esophagus, diarrhea, weight loss—all of which will dissipate upon termination of the treatments. So far none of these has occurred.

When we walked into the new James Cancer Hospital last week, I saw state-of-the-art equipment and highly trained personnel functioning with skill and caring. Visiting briefly with a man who will journey from Mt. Vernon to Columbus (more than a hundred miles round-trip) for the next thirty-three days for radiation, it dawned on me that this facility is the only one of its kind between New York and Houston—and it's less than three miles from our home. I wondered why anyone in central Ohio would go anywhere else. What a blessing to have this facility and expertise so close.

DECEMBER 21, 1991

Never a dull moment. Two days after I last wrote, I suffered excruciating abdominal pain, diarrhea, and vomiting. It was a nocturnal attack, and by noon the next day, I was improved and able to read for a 4:00 p.m. program at church. The following day, the radiation oncologist ordered a blood test to determine my white count, which had sunk to one-half of normal. The result was to call off treatments for a couple of days, but by Thursday, when they were to resume, I was a mighty sick patient at University Hospital.

For the first twenty-four hours, it appeared surgery would be necessary to remove a couple of feet of my ileum, but there was a reluctance because of the possibility the radiation had damaged my bowel. In a small number of cases, radiation changes the character of bowel tissue in such a way that it's unable to retain a suture. That would be disastrous and would undoubtedly result in a colostomy. A modest risk, but why take any risk if they could get me through the acute stage? So hour by hour they watched and waited—and I pulled through.

> The doctors were originally afraid he had a blockage, a perforation, an abscess, or a burst appendix. It seemed probable he was headed for surgery. Finally about 8:30 p.m., they told me to go home, and they'd call if surgery were imminent. In the meantime, Chuck was put on intravenous antibiotics.
>
> It was most interesting to stand by Chuck's bed with the doctors as they talked among themselves. They were all very good to me, kept me informed, and included me in their discussions. The surgeons were saying it was imperative they operate, while the medical doctors said, yes, but . . . Then they'd all go out of the room and stand around the records station discussing technicalities. After that they'd come back to talk with me.
>
> What feelings I had at that point! I was filled with fear for Chuck's life. I didn't want him to be operated on and cut down more, nor did

I want whatever he had to be life-threatening. At least I didn't have to be anxious about his doctors. I knew he was in good hands.

There is a new law that requires the hospital or the doctor to have a copy of the patient's living will, so that hospital personnel know his or her desires about heroic measures. After Chuck survived the night, he had an opportunity, over the next five days of his hospitalization, to talk with his doctors about his wishes. It was so hard to hear him say he didn't want anything that would prolong the agony for me and the family—that he wanted us to be able to get on with our lives. I understood his feelings, but my life is with him and I'm in no hurry to get on with it without him. I'm confident that when I must I will, but there's no rush. I do know I don't want Chuck's misery continued if he is suffering or out of it with no hope for a good quality of life. Tough talk, necessary talk.

Over the next few days, I had various tests—x-rays, CT scan, an upper gastrointestinal (GI) series with small intestine follow-through, and finally a colonoscopy, all with no specific results. Perhaps I had radiation enteritis or a raging infection of some sort. Crohn's disease was mentioned as a possibility. Except for the possible relationship to the radiation, this whole episode seems to be unrelated to cancer, but it certainly represents another item on an already full plate.

DECEMBER 30, 1991

We are back from Christmas in D.C. It took a lot of courage on Chuck's part to go, as he really was exhausted from his "hot belly" and was apprehensive as to whether it would return. He was determined to go, though, and how grateful we were to have Christmas with the whole family.

When we arrived in Washington, I wondered if we had made the right choice, as Chuck was tired, drawn, lackluster, and noticeably trying to put his best foot forward. In addition to that, he was having trouble swallowing, an effect of the radiation to his neck. He picked up in the next couple of days, though, as he learned to withdraw and renew himself, rejoining all of us after some rest. It was a glorious, bittersweet time. There were no long faces, but there was an understanding beneath the surface that this was a special Christmas. We were all together; who knows what other years might bring?

The morning we left Washington to drive to Morgantown, West Virginia, which is halfway home, all was well. Chuck, Karen, and I walked and packed the car, and the two of us took off feeling fulfilled and grateful. After about an hour or so, Chuck said he had a "gut" ache, and although he didn't want to alarm me, he said it felt the same way it had when he was in the hospital. His doctors had told him it was OK to go to Washington, but that if he developed a fever or aching gut, we should hightail it home. We decided before we reached Morgantown that we would drive straight on through to Columbus. Even if his trouble stopped, we'd be uneasy if it reappeared in the middle of the night. We'd much rather be where his doctors were. It was then 3:30, so we'd be home by 7:00 p.m. It was a good decision. When we arrived home, Chuck was exhausted and feeling miserable. If that had happened in Morgantown, I would have been terribly upset and frightened, and Chuck would have been even more anxious.

Chuck talked with Cindi, who felt he was in no danger. She wanted to see him today. This morning she told him she is still concerned about the ileum and wants him to have an upper GI series. If there's no evidence of inflammation or narrowing, she will be assured the problem is resolving itself. However, if there is further stricture, the only thing to do is surgery. Enough time has passed that if surgery is necessary, the bowel is less susceptible to falling apart from the effects of the radiation.

In the meantime, he is to stop his high intake of fibers, just to be kind to the bowel. Of course, this worsens the constipation that comes with the codeine, so now he must take care of it with enemas, mineral oil, and suppositories. Dr. Cindi has talked with the radiation oncologist, and they have decided to wait until the tests are done before starting the radiation again.

So we are watching and waiting, but I know all Chuck's doctors are careful and doing their best. I told Dr. Cindi how grateful I am for her care of Chuck, and she took my hand, saying she was always available to me for anything she could do. Chuck has a winner in her!

DECEMBER 31, 1991

"Teach your wife to be a widow." That's what I've advised men as I worked with them on their estates and life insurance. And so I have done with Martha. For years we divided the financial responsibilities of our family. Martha had her own funds and her own accounts. She's done a superb job. Never once have I had to bail her out or toss her a life preserver.

Today I handed everything over to her; she will be responsible for all the family finances. We have talked about this for months and concluded that we would make the transition effective with the new year. It's best we do this while I'm here to monitor the transition, to hold her hand while she assumes the entire responsibility. We spent more than three hours together at the desk, and as we worked I tried to imagine what it would have been like for her if she had had these matters dropped into her lap after I was gone, when she was already dealing with emotions of overwhelming dimensions.

I feel rather empty as I write, as if I had swum to shore and pulled myself out of the waters of the passing stream.

> I wasn't much help to Chuck today, because I didn't have any sense of humor when he tried to be humorous about the finances. I'm sorry, but I was too involved with his state of health and the symbolism involved with what we were doing. It was hard for Chuck and hard for me. It symbolizes separation, and I don't like it.

3

The Paths Diverge

(1992–1994)

At a certain point the Wheelers realized that no matter how close their relationship, they were on the ultimate existential journey; Martha could no longer accompany Chuck on his path, and he was unable to travel Martha's. "No one can die for me, and no one can be a widow for Martha," Chuck wrote. At this juncture their diaries became more introspective and the differences in their coping mechanisms became more apparent. The couple contended not only with Chuck's frightening physical changes and the encroachment of death, but also with unexpected communications problems that resulted in grievous misunderstandings and sometimes made it difficult for them to comfort one another. At a time when they expected to be most supportive of each other's needs, they were often out of touch with what those needs really were.

Pain control became paramount during this stage of Chuck's illness. His pain was managed by a surgically implanted morphine pump to which few others had access. This "miracle pump" gave him significant relief and allowed Chuck to participate in life far past the time many other patients were able to. He credited the pump with extending his life and enhancing its quality. He desperately wanted others suffering cancer pain to be aware of the options available; he saw no virtue in terminal pain and therefore included considerable information about pain control in this portion of his journal.

The arc of the Wheelers' pilgrimage together encompassed the mundane and "things above." There was virtually no question—physical, psychological, spiritual, personal, or financial—the two of them did not address. Readers will see a clear progression, not only of disease, but also of faith, hope, and above all, love. Chuck and Martha's story movingly demonstrates how life can be fully lived even in the presence of death.

JANUARY 9, 1992

It's been a long time since we had any good news on the health front. But yesterday was different. After privately speculating

98

THE PATHS DIVERGE 99

that I was headed for a surgical solution to my ileum problem, we were elated to have a call from Dr. Cindi, advising us that the results of my GI series indicated, as she said, "Everything is resolved with no complications." Now all we have to be concerned about is cancer.

JANUARY 13, 1992

Cindi calls it "the dwindles." It's an apt description of how I feel. The dictionary defines *dwindle* as "to become gradually less until little remains, to diminish." Well, there remains a lot, but I am dwindling. My weight and appetite are both diminishing. My morning weight used to be between 128 and 130. When I was released from the hospital, after being on various restricted diets, I weighed 121, and in the intervening four weeks I have gained only a pound or two.

My appetite varies, but last night I had a startling experience when I looked at my dinner and realized I was going to have to encourage myself to eat. It was our traditional Sunday-night dinner—an overstuffed steak sandwich on pumpernickel, and raw vegetables. I helped Martha prepare the meal. I now know I put too many veggies on the plates, and the abundance turned me away. Even after Martha took some of the food off my plate, my normal appetite wasn't there.

It was a new and strange situation for me, and for the first time in my life, I understood the loss of appetite. It's an involuntary condition—another one of those situations where one feels overcome by external forces and unable to do what one rationally knows needs to be done.

JANUARY 18, 1992

Memories of my recent hospitalization are fading away, but one remains. It was renewed and reinforced last week when I returned for my GI series.

It takes a long time for the barium to work its way through the small intestine to the ileum and then to the colon. In the radiation department, a strange new setting for me, I felt very much alone and aware of my separation from Martha. I didn't know where she was, and she didn't know where I was. My inability to communicate with her was foremost in my mind. It was like being overseas, all strange and so out of touch.

My mind and emotions were deeply at peace. I had a profound sense of well-being, supported by some invisible force of goodness and appropriateness. I didn't want it to end, and I wasn't disquieted by the periodic interruptions by the technicians. I wished Martha could be there to share this most satisfying experience, but she wasn't, and I accepted the fact. I wondered if this were like heaven.

During these last years, I have been hospitalized at University Hospital three times and have had one outpatient procedure. This last period differs in one notable manner. There is a new feeling of warmth, punctuated by what seemed to me to be an increased amount of touching, hand-holding, and even hugging. It is all very positive and helpful and gives me a real sense of being the recipient of sincere caring and love.

JANUARY 22, 1992

Dr. Cindi called last evening. It's mighty reassuring to know she's concerned and caring enough to initiate a contact.

It was my understanding that Stan would turn to chemotherapy if radiation proved unfruitful. Obviously I want to know much more before submitting to it. Dr. Cindi said she had talked with Dr. Arthur H., a pain specialist, who suggested various medications to use before I progressed to the point of seeing him. They also had talked about other medications for the long haul. Perhaps there are several alternatives before we get to chemo, if we need it at all. That sounds good to me.

> Chuck and I are clearly traveling two paths now. He seems more philosophical to me, and I seem more assertive to him. Chuck is dealing with what his eternal future will be and is excited about it. But who can define eternal life? The journey he is on is a journey only he can experience. I don't want to take any of his excitement away from him.

> Because of his viewpoint, he is more relaxed about matters that might have concerned him at an earlier time. His priorities are on a higher plane now, and perhaps his life is too short to get upset over mundane matters. That all sounds terribly vague, and I don't want to paint the picture that Chuck doesn't care about politics, economics, or what's going on in life, because he does. It's just that I'm not used to his being so calm or so difficult to engage in discussion. Sometimes it feels as if I'm hitting a soft pillow, and that's frustrating.

> Chuck, on the other hand, experiences me as being more assertive and more harsh. Assertiveness is OK, but being told I seem more

harsh is very hard on me, because I wouldn't knowingly do that to Chuck.

As Chuck thinks about what's ahead for him, I think about what's ahead for me, and it's hard for us not to plan these two events together. I can't imagine not snuggling or holding. I can't imagine fixing only my own cereal or eating alone, or planning anything that doesn't include Chuck. I know I'll keep busy; I know I'll get involved, but I don't know in what way. I just know it will happen, and when I really stop to think about it, I realize I've been subtly reaching out to friends in areas that don't include Chuck.

As I write, I understand more fully the two paths and the impact they are having on our lives. To ignore these paths would be to ignore a new dimension in our lives—a dimension that makes us sad, but a dimension that makes us grow.

JANUARY 29, 1992

Everything has a price. Pain control is no exception. Gradually through the months I have increased my medication to deal with the pain in my lower back and neck. Last month's radiation was designed to enable me to back off the medication. I'd love to. For pain, as well as for other problems of long duration, I'm now taking sixteen pills a day. Ridiculous!

The radiation enteritis caused us to abandon that approach and return to medication. We have discontinued the Voltaren and gone to Tylenol 4 with double the amount of codeine in Tylenol 3. We've been increasing my dosage to eight pills per day with great results. The dose manages my pain very well, to the point that override is limited to four or five times a day, and is usually brief. But, holy mackerel, I'm paying the price of a constipation I've never known. Dr. Cindi calls it colon paralysis. Laxatives, mineral oil, and stool softeners are of little benefit. I have to take an enema every second or third day.

Such a life! Things could be worse, however, and probably will be.

FEBRUARY 3, 1992

Through the months I've been seeing Stan, he's held out his father-in-law, himself a victim of prostate cancer, as one we might emulate. His father-in-law died last week. I feel as if I have lost a friend, in spite of the fact I never met him. I feel as if a piece of me is gone. How ironic he should die of prostate cancer, the very disease against which Stan labors and struggles daily. Somehow it doesn't seem fair.

FEBRUARY 6, 1992

Chuck says I seem terribly stressed. I knew my body felt stressed, especially in the last week. I had Valium I could take, but I kept thinking I could manage without it. I told myself I did well during the tense time Chuck was in the hospital. I couldn't understand why I felt so stressed out now. When we were on our walk, Chuck helped me see I haven't discharged yet all the stress of December. My gut feeling says that's true.

His dwindles affect me more than I realize. He becomes upset over matters that never would have bothered him as they do now. For example, the *Wall Street Journal* comes every day, and he feels he must read it. When he doesn't read it as thoroughly as he used to, it puts stress on him. Instead of reading the paper, he wants to read books he never had time to read before, but since he paid for the *Journal* subscription, he feels guilty if he just browses through it. It's not worth the stress, so I agreed to cancel the paper. As long as it's here, he'll feel pressured, and I don't want that.

Chuck's more introspective, and I recognize that. I wouldn't trade our deep conversations for anything. I'm not really complaining; I'm just realizing his outside interests are dwindling, too.

FEBRUARY 13, 1992

We saw Stan yesterday in what turned out to be a very rocky session. We have heard others say how much difficulty they have with him, but it has never happened to us. He was almost impossible—critical, defensive, short, irritated. Something was wrong, for sure. My PSA, which been 11 and 15.6 in November, is now 4. I was skeptical and asked for a repeat. He agreed to it, all the while saying that the difference between 4 and 30 is meaningless, and above 30 calls for specific attention.

I left confused and went to radiation oncology. Dr. G. was great—patient, relaxed, and caring—and he dealt with us as if I were his only patient. I told him I was gun-shy about completing the radiation series. Although he doubts the enteritis came from the radiation, he did admit that my entire experience had been somewhat atypical, and as long as I am able to manage my pain with codeine, he agreed not to resume treatment.

Having cooled down somewhat, we returned to Stan's office

and had it out with him. We suspect he is somewhat vexed about Dr. Cindi having gotten into the act. He indicated he considers it his responsibility to deal with the issue of pain. There seems to be no explanation of the precipitous drop in my PSA. There are lots of unanswered questions in medicine.

FEBRUARY 17, 1992

I've been very eager to see Bob, not only for my arthritis, but also for my general well-being. I've been uptight, harsh, preoccupied, and forgetful. I couldn't settle down, and I wanted to be sure my brain was working properly after my surgery.

Bob told me in no uncertain terms that I'm OK; I'm acting normally for a woman whose husband is dying. He asked me if I needed stronger Valium, and I said no. I only need to take what I have. I'm uneasy about taking it, because I feel I can be strong. He told me to take it when I needed it, whether it was regularly or sporadically. When all this is over, I won't need it anymore.

I followed his advice for a couple of days, but then I felt like my old self again, so I stopped taking the medicine. It's difficult for me to take a medication for stress. I feel guilty about it. I realize, however, that for me to fully enjoy each day with Chuck, I need to avoid stress overload. After all, he doesn't say, "I think I'll rise above my pain and not take codeine," so why do I think I should rise above my pain without medication? Having said that doesn't take away from the fact that my faith gives me great strength. I know, though, that when I'm on overload, even the Lord has a hard time beating down the wall. When I'm overstressed, I find it hard to pray because I can't get myself out of the way.

I now understand it's OK for me to be stressed and to deal with it medically. I don't have try to prove to myself and to the whole world that I'm strong.

FEBRUARY 18, 1992

Several days ago I had the deeply moving experience of giving CPR [cardiopulmonary resuscitation] to a ninety-year-old man who, when I arrived on the scene, had neither pulse nor respiration. I administered CPR for about ten minutes until the squad arrived. His heart monitor showed no activity, but after electric shock and other treatment, his heart started again.

As I pumped away on his chest, many thoughts went through my mind, one of which was the difference between being struck down in a fleeting moment and having a terminal disease that affords the patient the gift of time to deal with it and grow. One of my growth experiences occurred after I found out about the change in my PSA. I have always been an in-charge person. In a subtle way I have been in charge of my disease. I have known and interpreted in my own way the numbers that represent the progression of illness—PSA values, medication dosages, the number of months of probable benefit from androgen deprivation therapy, perhaps even speculation about the month of my death. What's more, my in-chargeness has been acted out by attempting to communicate all these things to my family and our friends.

Now, having accepted the inevitable upward march of my PSA, I have been confronted with a decrease in the numbers, and Ole Dad, the number cruncher, the planner, the expert on cause and effect, is confused. And if that isn't confusion enough, Stan says I could go on like this for months, or the bottom could fall out next week. It all depends on where the metastasis lands.

At the age of seventy-one, I don't see much hope in making myself into a less in-charge person, but I believe it's important I reconsider what it is I'm in charge of. It appears to me I should make a major effort to be less in charge of numbers and their meaning. I need to be in charge of today, and live it, reporting accurately the pain I experience, taking my medication, controlling my diet, and maintaining my level of health. The rest belongs to others, although I will continue to be an informed participant.

FEBRUARY 26, 1992

Early the other evening Dr. Cindi called just to ask how we were doing. What a dear, kind lady and physician. I told her about the recent episode with Stan. She said she had no problem at all with Stan being in charge of my pain.

MARCH 2, 1992

It appears that my present dosage of eight Tylenol 4 capsules each day represents a lot of codeine, although it wouldn't surprise me if I were to increase to ten or twelve per day, the maximum dosage, in the foreseeable future. My pain is overriding the present dosage every day, although it is not intolerable.

Bob told Martha recently that codeine has a side effect of alternating euphoria and depression, although he qualified his use of the word *depression* to indicate a downer, a sense of dejection as opposed to a true, clinical depression. I'm experiencing some of this. Even as I write, I'm high, euphoric, happy. I'm content in spite of today's pain. It seems to me that, on balance, my euphoria is more pronounced than the down experience of the down days.

MARCH 20, 1994

We made reservations back in early November to come to Florida. We rented a condo on the beach for two weeks, and when we made the reservations, we made sure the management knew both the circumstances of Chuck's health and that we might have to cancel. As I sit here in the condo, writing on my word processor, I'm consumed with gratitude that we're here.

We took nine days to arrive, stopping to visit friends, Don and Betty Vlcek, on the way down. The Vlceks winter in South Carolina; they are the finest and dearest friends anyone could have. While we were at their place, Chuck had three really tough days, dealing with pain, weakness, and fatigue. Betty and Don understood completely and let Chuck go at his own pace. Chuck's problems didn't bother his bridge playing, however, as he and Don beat the socks off Betty and me.

This was a difficult few days for me, and it took all my will power not to try to protect Chuck. I think the most telling time was when we were attending Don and Betty's little church on Sunday morning. Usually Chuck sits at the end of the pew, so he can position himself in the corner and support his back. That day he wasn't on the end, and he didn't have his pillow with him—he resists taking it to church. It was clear to me that he was having a hard time getting up and down and that he was hurting. Part way through the service, he moved to the other end of our pew where he could have support. I was torn between moving down with him, since I wanted to sit with him, or staying where I was, so as not to call any more attention to his discomfort. I decided I would move down as soon as there was a break in the service and I could do so easily. But before that time, Chuck came back to my side. It's at moments like this that my stomach knots. I don't like seeing him react to pain.

Before we left home, I stopped taking my Valium. I felt OK, and we were going on vacation, so I thought I wouldn't need it. How short-

sighted of me. Sure, we were going on vacation, but the cancer and all
its ramifications were going with us, which of course meant my stress
level was still high. This became evident at Chuck's sister's, where I
got on overload very quickly. I thought I could handle it and never
considered taking my medication until the day we left. We departed
on Saturday, and now it's the following Friday, the first day I haven't
had any tightening in my stomach. I have felt more like myself each
day, and now it's total. Bob says I can take four pills a day, but I find
two is plenty.

MARCH 21, 1992

Now the latest is an attack of vertigo. It awakened me about
3:15 a.m., here at Hillsboro Beach, thirteen hundred miles
from home. I haven't had such an attack since 1966 and really
can't account for this one. During the night, we thought of all
sorts of scenarios, mostly about getting back to Columbus and
Dr. Cindi, but after sitting up a while, I was able to lie down
again, and in due course I fell asleep. This morning I'm fine,
and my equilibrium is about as usual. I guess we'll live one day
at a time and see how things go.

MARCH 24, 1992

Several days ago, Melody Williams, our associate rector, suggested we
turn our faces toward Jerusalem as we enter Lent. At that time, I had
never really entered into how God must have felt as He watched His
son marching to the music He heard. I always knew that God must
have hurt and been filled with anguish, but to me, it was what was
supposed to be.

How insensitive I was, or at least how ignorant! At this time in my
life, I find myself seeing the road on which Chuck is traveling, and
I'm powerless to do anything about it. This must have been the way
God felt about the path His only son was taking. He knew that for
human beings like me to understand the message Jesus had been sent
to deliver, Jesus had to submit to the humiliation, to ask to be spared
from this suffering and torture, and to die and rise again. How God
must have felt, how He must have hurt, how He must have wished He
could change the scenario!

When one believes in eternal life, there is peace, but that peace
does not take away the pain of watching a loved one slip away or suffer, nor does it alleviate the pain of separation. I know Chuck has to
die before he can enter eternal life, but I hurt to watch him walk the

path that leads to our separation. I believe and I know that God understands my hurt, and I feel His love. I also know that Jesus is telling me He too was filled with hurt as He traveled the road to Jerusalem, but the hurt had its purpose. He is with Chuck on his road, giving him strength and courage, just as a marathon runner receives encouragement along the way.

I turn my face toward Jerusalem with a broader insight, and I thank God. I know that, although Chuck and I are on separate roads, there is a bridge of faith that connects our paths.

APRIL 12, 1992

Occasionally I wonder if I'll wear out the blanket on my bed by repeatedly throwing it off during the night, only to pull it up a little later. It's been forty-four months since the orchiectomy, but still the hot flashes persist, more often during the night. Stan warned me about them, although he indicated they'd probably dissipate. So far they haven't.

APRIL 18, 1992

We've been home from Florida for over two weeks, and I haven't written anything. In a way that's good, but I think it's important to write when things are as status quo as they can be. It's good to know that it isn't just one crisis after another when cancer is part of your everyday life. Most of the time the knowledge of cancer is there, but it is easy to live with as we go about our lives, walking, talking, reading, associating with others, and blessing each day we're together. We deal with the adjustments we have to make, and we evaluate how Chuck can get the most enjoyment out of the energy he has.

One of Chuck's friends who was diagnosed with prostate cancer in 1989 is in bad shape, and at this time all that can be done for him is to keep him comfortable. We hurt for him and his family. Today was a bonus day for us, however, as we changed our closets over from winter to spring and summer clothes. We remembered that when we put those clothes away last year, we wondered if Chuck would be taking his out again—and he did!

APRIL 28, 1992

What a day this has been! A great day it has been in so many ways, but this morning we were hit in the face by a front-page *Columbus Dispatch* article about our good friend Stan. This is the man who, from the first time we met him in 1986, won our confidence and our

hearts. Today it was announced he is charged with scholarly misconduct in his research. His clinical practice is not involved. Chuck and
I are stunned, because we know him as a man who is dedicated to
finding the cause and cure of prostate cancer. Stan is only forty-four
years old, but he has devoted himself to the problem of prostate cancer and is world-renowned for his work. So we grieve for him and
wonder just what happened. We will most likely never know. For ourselves, we know he is a caring and dedicated man, and we hurt for
him and pray that this in no way keeps him from going on with his
research or interferes with his desire to whip this disease.

For ourselves, we feel alone, as Stan is the one who has given
Chuck almost six years since the prostatectomy and forty-four
months since the orchiectomy, and both those figures have beaten the
statistics. Stan has been open, honest, caring, and all the while has
understood our desire to enjoy each and every minute we have together. He has encouraged us to do what we want to do; he has never been
pessimistic, only realistic in helping us to look ahead, so we wouldn't
miss any opportunity by being hesitant. I'm grateful Stan has done
what he has for Chuck, for these six years have been wonderful in
many, many ways, and we both attribute that to Stan. We pray he and
his family will come out of this situation whole.

MAY 1, 1992

We've heard, ever since we first learned I had cancer, that others don't know what to say and so say little or, in their discomfort, withdraw and become distant. We have experienced
some of the silence, although not nearly as much as we had
anticipated, and essentially none of the withdrawal. As a matter of fact, we have been supported by the willingness of many
of our friends to address the disease and the effects it is having
on us. Some have even gone out of their way to say things—
often kind and sensitive things—things one would expect to
hear after one has died.

Chuck Adkins, the chief engineer for the Central Ohio
Radio Reading Service, made such a thoughtful comment
today—a comment that took much courage on his part and
resulted in great joy to me. He inquired how I am feeling and
what the outlook is, and then added, "Chuck, I'm going to miss
you." He turned and left, and I followed him down the hall and
embraced him in gratitude. It was very satisfying.

MAY 3, 1992

I so enjoy making all kinds of bread, but kneading has become increasingly difficult because of the arthritis in my hands. Arthritis may not be fatal, but it is painful and debilitating. I haven't liked to admit that kneading the bread is painful, and I've been able to avoid doing so because Chuck has enjoyed doing the kneading for me, and we've made a terrific team in creating breads and rolls. The other day he was on the phone when it was time to knead the bread, so I did it. It was really a jolt to me to realize how hard it was to do; then for the next two days my hands were swollen and painful.

Chuck and I had talked about my needing a breadmaker or heavy-duty mixer someday. I had inquired about breadmakers and was unhappy they made only one loaf at a time. I like to make several loaves so I can take them to church to be used for calling on new members or to give away to friends. The machine I thought I wanted had a horrendous price tag—more than three hundred dollars. However, we got ours at a discount house that was having a sale, so it cost somewhat less. It was Chuck's Mother's Day present to me, and what a beautiful present it was. What makes it more than a material gift is the fact that he and I can enjoy using it together. We can both rejoice in how the machine kneads the dough. If I'd bought the bread-maker because Chuck could no longer do that chore or because he was no longer here to do it, the joy would not be there. In fact, I would use it only with tears running down my face. I'm sure when I use it after Chuck is gone and no longer standing beside me watching, there will still be tears, but they won't be as blinding, because I'll have such good memories surrounding the event. It may seem like a small thing, but it's not.

Today I had another insight. I have accepted that Chuck is ready for bed at 7:30 p.m. He stays alert and awake until 9:30 when we have company or are with friends, but it is difficult. Today I realized that I hadn't emotionally accepted that Chuck's energy leaves him sponta-neously and unannounced, and that when it happens, he is wiped out. Though my mind has accepted the facts, it has taken longer for my guts to do so. I realize from past experience that accepting something intellectually is far from doing so emotionally. As long as I stopped short of emotional acceptance, I was not only ripping myself up, but also failing to help Chuck.

Tonight's thoughts also include how special snuggling is, how spe-cial hugging is, how special kissing is, how special it is to look into Chuck's eyes and to say, "I love you." It's so special just to be togeth-

er. We aren't as we were in our twenties, thirties, forties, fifties, or six-
ties in energy or lovemaking, but I can say that we enjoy every way
and every minute we have to express our love to one another. Our
bliss is being together, sharing thoughts and opinions (and we don't
always agree; that would be uninteresting), sharing our religious experiences, and taking our "buddy baths."

This cancer is a journey I'd just as soon we didn't have to take, but
it is an enriching journey for us both—hard and hurtful but enriching.
That's a dichotomy, but it's real.

MAY 4, 1992

How in the world can one sleep soundly for ten hours and get
up feeling so tired? After breakfast we walked to church for
silent prayers and then home again. Now, at noon, I'm still
fatigued.

Footnote: It's midafternoon, and my strength is back again.
It leaves unexpectedly and returns similarly. Crazy!

MAY 14, 1992

Still no word from Stan. It seems to me he has an obligation to
his patients to communicate with them. It is all very peculiar
and leaves us feeling as if we're dangling out on the end of a
limb.

MAY 21, 1992

Stan called today. I had written him seeking his advice about
what I should do. We had an unhurried, warm, and friendly
conversation. He told me of the metamorphosis in his life—his
new unwillingness to work ninety or a hundred hours per
week—his desire to withdraw from research and to focus his
attention on the practice of urology, particularly in training his
patients as opposed to training residents and interns. He
implied he would ultimately be leaving Columbus to practice
elsewhere.

It is clear there is much more going on here than scholarly
misconduct. It's evident he has been brought up short and has
reassessed his modus operandi and his whole life. He says there
is nothing more important than his wife and family, and he
mentioned earlier comments I had made about the importance
of seeking peace by saying, "I want that peace you refer to."

He referred me to three other urologists on staff, not in order of their professional competence but ranked by their personalities, in order of suitability for us. His choice was Bill B. Then I called Dr. Cindi and asked her if she could recommend someone with whom she would be comfortable and with whom she could work effectively. (We are aware she had difficulty with Stan.) She said she would recommend Bill B. That was enough for me, so I made an appointment and will see Bill on June 3. He's my guy.

I'm relieved and completely satisfied. I had no desire to start again to build a team. We had built our team around Stan at the University and James hospitals, and I was determined to stay with them and at those facilities. Even if Stan had unexpectedly said he intended to open a new practice in Columbus and to refer patients to another hospital, I would have been hard-pressed to go with him, although I confess it would have been a difficult choice.

MAY 22, 1992

When I talked with Dr. Cindi yesterday, I told her of my increasing pain. While it's far from excruciating or disabling, it was overriding my Tylenol 4 every day and disturbing my sleep. We decided to stay with the Tylenol, but to substitute Percocet for the last dose before retiring, first a single pill for a week and two thereafter.

MAY 26, 1992

Today was a peculiar day. It began while I was boarding a bus to go downtown for lunch with a good friend. The first step onto the bus was a high one. I got my foot onto the step, but didn't have the strength in that leg to hoist myself up, nor could I raise my foot from the step and return it to the street, enabling me to start over. I felt stranded and helpless for a moment until I was able to grasp something inside the bus and literally drag myself onto the step. It was startling and frightening to be failed by my legs.

Then after Bud and I left the restaurant, I started to feel insecure and unsure. My equilibrium was problematic, particularly when I stepped onto the escalator or changed directions. The atmosphere around me seemed unusually noisy, confusing, and intimidating. I didn't faint, but I wondered if I were going to collapse and if I'd be coherent enough to get myself to the hospital. It was a full block away, but I managed to get to the bus shelter and to wait a seemingly interminable thirty minutes for the bus.

Upon arriving home, I had a great sense of relief and security. Martha and I held each other, and I tried to describe what had happened.

MAY 27, 1992

I see Chuck as others probably don't. I see his pallor and the tiredness in his eyes. I sense his concern as he experiences the dwindles, more pain, and other unusual feelings. He tells me when he notices changes in himself, and I tell him when I see him looking more pale or tired. There's no use trying to fool one another. After forty-eight years, we know each other inside and out.

My heart breaks as I see him making concessions, because I know he doesn't until it's absolutely necessary. He hasn't wanted to take a pillow into church, but now he has three stashed away in different locations so one will be handy no matter where he sits. In fact, he now doesn't go anywhere without a pillow for his back. That's good, but I know he has to hurt quite a bit to do it, and that makes me sad.

Both of us are on edge. We are more quick to disagree on some little point, which is not like us. We have learned to recognize what we're doing and to back off. Later we discuss it, and it's usually difficult for us to recall why it happened. It's another aspect of the disease, I guess, although we know it's not the disease itself. It's only us as we deal with it.

We know now that Stan is gone, as far as his practice is concerned. Chuck has been referred to Bill B. There's probably nothing more he can do but follow Chuck and work with Dr. Cindi on his pain medication, but it's nice to know Chuck will have a relationship with a urologist if he needs one again.

JUNE 1, 1992

In two more days, I'll have my first appointment with Bill B., and I am eager for it. It's somewhat disconcerting to have to start all over again with a new urologist, but we have accepted Stan's withdrawal from practice and look with confidence to a new relationship with Bill. Even more, I look to this appointment for a timely evaluation. We haven't had one since February, and I feel as if things are changing. Perhaps it is all in my imagination. I guess we just need an update.

Gosh, I'm emotional these days. I have always been easily moved to tears, but it seems as if I've become even more so in recent months. It doesn't take much to start the tears rolling—holding Martha, praying, thinking about our kids and my love for them, thinking about the wonderful relationship Martha and I have had, listening to beautiful music, worshipping, writing from the heart, thinking about the hurt my cancer brings to Martha and the children, reflecting on our friends, thinking about my death and my belief in a new and exciting dimension—and on and on.

Were it not that this seems only an enhancement of what has long been a characteristic of mine, I'd wonder if it might not be attributed to the medication. I just don't know.

JUNE 4, 1992

All sorts of unexpected things occurred at our first appointment with Bill B. We like him very much. Among other things, he said, "I'll sit and talk with you as long as you need to talk." Our kind of guy!

He seems to shy away from chemo; he see no value in "being ill from it for eight months if you expect to live for twelve." He commented about several other experimental drugs, but said they too would make me very ill. Bill suggested we begin Flutamide to knock out the testosterone that originates in the adrenals, in spite of the fact that it will probably be a useless effort. There is a hypothesis that taking the medicine after an orchiectomy has no value, but Bill says that inasmuch as the potential side effects are so modest, why not give it a try? Statistically, if it is effective, it seems to add about seven months to one's life. That seems worthwhile, so now, adding the Flutamide, I'm consuming twenty-one pills every day at a total cost of three hundred dollars a month.

He was very specific with us, especially since this was our first appointment, and we appreciated his candor. He urged us to get our affairs in order, and we were pleased to assure him they already were. We questioned him about how long he expects me to live, and of course he replied that I might live as long as five years, but statistically speaking, he would expect me to die within a year. It was not easy to hear, especially for Martha.

Then we discussed pain. His idea of pain management is dif-

ferent from Stan's. He simply called in the chronic-pain management team, and they arrived three strong, including their
chief honcho, Dr. Arthur H. Dr. Cindi had discussed me with
him as much as six months ago, but Arthur H. had said I wasn't
ready for him yet. So when he marched into Bill's office, we
knew this was for real. They proceeded to discontinue all my previous medication and to substitute MS Contin twice a day,
Trilisate twice a day; they retained the Percocet for acute pain
breakthroughs. The plan is to try these levels and adjust as necessary before we go East next week.

> The job of the chronic-pain service is to see that Chuck has as little
> pain as possible, while still allowing him to function and have a good
> quality of life. They know pain deprives patients of enjoyment, and
> they feel there is a delicate balance between too little medication and
> too much. Fortunately they rely on the patient to tell them how much
> pain he has, rather than on their own opinions.
>
> During our conversation, they gave us cards with the phone num-
> bers to call day and night, including weekends and holidays. There
> will always be someone on duty who can get Chuck's chart on com-
> puter and know what to prescribe at that time. What a great comfort!

JUNE 8, 1992

I suffered a major pain breakthrough in church yesterday, about
an 8 or 9 on a scale of 1 to 10. Thank God for Percocet. It's
clear that pain has become a more significant matter these days.
It is interesting to watch it progress, although I expect it to
plateau one of these days. That seems to be the way it goes.

JUNE 9, 1992

> I thought we were all set. How wrong I was! The new medication didn't
> deal with Chuck's pain. The pain was always there, with none of the pre-
> vious peaks and valleys. He spent two miserable nights, after which he
> called the pain-service people, who upped his medication. That helped
> for only a short time, so he called again, and they increased the dosage
> once more. Today he called a third time, as the pain was still breaking
> through, and he was concerned about our going away for twelve days.
> They upped the dose again and said he should have no more trouble.
>
> It's been hard to watch him this week, as he has struggled with the
> pain and not wanted to cry wolf. I knew things were going to get
> worse, but I wasn't prepared to have him waken each morning feeling

miserable and hurting. He looks drawn. He walks every morning, but it's easy to see how difficult it is for him. I thought the pain people would help him have less pain. Now I understand that there has to be a trial period for the pain specialists to know where he actually is and to determine his base level of medication.

Today I had lunch with a good friend, Jan, who lost her husband, Jim, to cancer last October. We met for lunch or talked on the phone many times during Jim's illness and since his death. Today was her turn to minister to me, since I was lower than a snake's belly. She was able to assure me it was OK. I told her I wanted to take Chuck and run away and build a wall around us, so the cancer couldn't reach him. I just wanted to push it all away. It was a fleeting feeling but, oh, so real! Because she had been down this road, she understood, and she reminded me to be good to myself and to take care of myself. I assured her that I am and I will, because it's important both to me and to Chuck.

I've been terribly anxious, I've scolded myself, I've tried to be strong, and I've prayed, and still I'm just beside myself. Finally tonight I've accepted the fact that I have to let Chuck have his physical pain, just as he lets me have my emotional pain.

JUNE 14, 1992

Martha's pain and stress continue to cause me pain and stress. She can't deal with it consistently well. It takes only the slightest negative event or comment to set her back, losing much of the ground she has so laboriously won. And when she hurts, I hurt. We talk about it a lot and realize we must move decisively into the kind of caring that faces the reality of our powerlessness to address one another's hurt, pain and stress, mine physical and Martha's emotional. We know that God knows we hurt and that He is with us in our pain. Can we do as much? Can we simply "be there," accepting one another's hurt and pain? I think so, but it takes conscious, unceasing effort from both of us.

Martha is my loving, caring, supporting friend and companion. Who will be hers when her time comes? She'll be so much more alone in her time of travail.

JUNE 26, 1992

Martha is at a luncheon, and I just returned from a noonday walk. I'm really very fatigued, and I feel weakness in my legs as never before. Early morning walks are easier, perhaps because of the freshness of just having slept nine or ten hours, perhaps because I haven't yet had the day's accumulation of medication. As I sat in my big black chair gathering energy, I could hardly see what I was reading, let alone comprehend it.

JULY 4, 1992

In looking back, I realize I'd been feeling trapped, but I didn't really know it. I was feeling mighty vulnerable the week before we left for Karen's. As we packed and loaded the car, I really didn't want Chuck to pick up anything that would cause a pain breakthrough, nor did I want to bug him about it. I was rushing because I wanted to finish packing our picnic dinner before Chuck loaded the car. I remember being short with him, which should have warned me I was uptight. When we arrived at our motel, I realized I hadn't brought any A1 Sauce or mayonnaise, so we went to the store to buy some. Then, as I was preparing the sandwiches, I remembered I'd left the turkey in the freezer at home, further evidence that I was preoccupied.

Chuck made a big concession our first night out. The only non-smoking room in the motel was on the second floor, which meant we had to drag our luggage upstairs. We had only one bag to carry up in addition to our "drugstore" bag, picnic, and books. Chuck insisted on carrying the heavy bag, even though I wanted to. I decided it was better to let him do it and see if it hurt him. Well, it did him in, and he needed more medication because of it. That was difficult for him to admit; these concessions sneak up on him and make him terribly unhappy. By then we were both stressed out.

When we arrived at Karen's, we had another episode between us because I suggested Chuck sit someplace where I thought he'd be more comfortable. We talked with Karen about my trying to be helpful and Chuck's needing to be independent. Because of Karen's listening to us struggle it out, Chuck said he'd ask for help to do things that are beyond his energy level, and I said I'd try not to bug him. That was all very good, but the next day it was clear that I was still nervous and picky. There was another spat in which I stung Chuck, and I knew it. I asked him and Karen what was making me act this way. In talking with them, I began to see that I felt backed into a corner by Chuck's illness. It took a couple of more episodes, however, before I could really begin to change my behavior. Karen was so helpful, so loving, and so good at listening.

The slightest thing will send Chuck and me into a tiff, and that is not like us. I have tried to be more gentle and understanding, and Chuck has tried not to get upset when I suggest something, but we don't know why we're reacting as we are. Yesterday, I gave him a dirty look in reaction to something he was doing. I apologized for it, but still I'm confused. Dirty looks are not something I do, but I sure did then, and it started us down a path of misunderstanding which racked us up for the rest of the day.

I think we both feel trapped and react because of that. We need to be more gentle and accepting of ourselves. I know I'm prone to lashing out when I feel cornered. I hope that understanding and realizing this will enable me to handle myself better.

JULY 7, 1992

Concessions, concessions, concessions. All I do is concede to cancer. Shit! Yesterday we made another concession, this one major.

For four years, Martha and I have trekked downtown every Friday morning at 7:00 a.m. to read the newspaper to the visually impaired over the Central Ohio Radio Reading Service. It was an activity we could do together, and it fed our souls. It has been enormously rewarding for both of us. In recent weeks, we've been dealing with my physical deterioration and an increase in stress. Nothing seemed to give us the relief we sought. Finally it dawned on us that our schedules were at least partially at fault. We weighed alternatives and considered the relief that might come if we eliminated this weekly obligation. The relief felt right and good. Reluctant though we were to discontinue this pleasurable activity, we did so, thus making a needed concession—again.

> Sitting in the position necessary for him to speak into the microphone was very difficult for Chuck, and by the end of the two hours of air time, he would be in agony, although he tried not to show it. His distress was obvious to me, however, because his face would be ashen. For me, the commitment was becoming more stressful, as I was juggling dates to accommodate Chuck's energy level, and I was a mess. It was very sad to resign, however.
>
> We really thought we were eliminating tension from our lives, but we find we are still wound up tightly, and the least little thing sets us

118

AFFIRMING THE DARKNESS

off. We have never been unable to talk to each other, and we have never had to be careful about what we said to one another. What is going on?

JULY 8, 1992

We've been attempting, with varying degrees of success, to relieve the grip of stress in our lives. Yesterday I said to Martha with great feeling, "You know, honey, I've never died before. This is a brand-new experience for me. It's a constant preoccupation." Martha's response was loving, accepting, and genuine. She said she anticipated my thoughts running in that direction and she welcomed my telling her how I feel about my own death, not as an abstraction, but as an approaching reality.

Nothing is more inevitable than my death; nothing is more final, irreversible, or irrevocable. For those fortunate enough to have the time to contemplate their own deaths, as I have, nothing is more preoccupying. Very few people seem willing to discuss or even think about these things. "Morbid," they say, as they change the subject. It hasn't been my good fortune to find others willing to share their thoughts and feelings about their own deaths.

There are also some constraints on me. I may be accused of possessing a death wish or of having some sort of sick fascination with the subject. This I totally deny, to the extent that I can deny it and still admit that death has become a preoccupation. I have no fear of death. I expect to slip into its ironclad grip with peace and acceptance. I have great feeling, however, for the hurt it will bring to Martha, Tom, Karen, and their families. I truly regret this hurt.

I wonder a lot about what happens in the world of the conscious and subconscious. In the written accounts of those who have died and returned to tell about it there seems to be a common thread of floating out of the physical body to a tunnel-like setting, the distant end of which is characterized by light and beauty. At the end of the tunnel, there is a Being who seeks an accounting for the days of one's life. Could this be Jesus? I wonder what I will say in response to His questions. I have no concern that my answers will be inadequate to the standards of the questioner, because whatever my shortcomings have been— and there have been many—I know and accept Jesus' assurance of forgiveness, love, and peace from God.

I wonder what the new life will be like. I'm sure there is no way to describe it in our earthly terms, but it will be new and joyful. I wonder if I will see and experience all those who have gone before me. When I consider that Mother and Dad and Martha's folks are only four of the billions of people who have left this planet, and that there are probably billions more from other planets, I know I'm in over my head. I'd better simply be patient for a while until I can understand the context of the next life. But I am fascinated.

I wonder if I'll be able to observe the events surrounding my death, and I wonder if there will be any way at all I can communicate with and influence those who remain behind. I think about the probable disappearance of time and how long it will seem before Martha joins me. I think about the disappearance of the daily necessities, such as breathing, gravity, and touch. I wonder if I'll be lonesome for Martha.

All this is about death, not about dying. Dying is a different matter, and in my case, it will probably be accompanied by lots of pain and indignity. If that's true, there will be much watching by all of us—they helplessly watching me and I helplessly watching them. I'm counting on the professionals to spare me from intolerable physical pain, but who will spare us all the pain of watching?

I have no concern for Martha's well-being nor for her ability to get along in the world without me. In spite of the extent to which we have depended on each other, I have total confidence in her acting alone—even if she does hang the toilet paper the wrong way!

I've long intended to read the books and materials on death and dying when the time came, but I doubt I'll do it now. I just think I can handle it myself, with the support of my family and a handful of special friends who have that unique ability to be there in the midst of all the helplessness and powerlessness.

JULY 16, 1992

Presence. It is so important for Martha and me to be together. We need each other's physical presence—in the kitchen when she is cooking or baking, in the den when we are relaxing or reading—anywhere. We also know the importance of being apart, of living our own lives individually but with others—as when one of us has lunch with others or when Martha is with her bridge group. We try to avoid clinging to each other, which would be easy to do. We urge one another to maintain contacts and relationships with others. But we prefer being together.

Touch. It is so important to touch one another. We hold hands as we walk or ride in the car. We snuggle both morning and night. We hug and hold each other a lot, sometimes risking the possibility of clinging when one of us feels insecure. We covet our daily buddy bath in the late afternoon before happy hour.

Presence and touch have never been more important in our lives.

JULY 21, 1992

The MS Contin continues to do well, but right now my perception of pain is like riding bareback from 3:30 a.m. until 10:00 a.m. After that, it's like riding with a saddle. Arthur says it takes four hours for the pill to begin to pump out its medication. Thus, my 6:00 a.m. dose begins to function around 10:00 a.m.

JULY 28, 1992

When will Martha and I *ever* get back in relationship, cease banging on each other, no longer have to guard every word against an unintended misstatement, and restore ourselves and each other from our frequent episodes of guilt? Why are we having these problems in the first place? Martha's upcoming MRI? Could the medications we take bring on changes in behavior or personality? Are our plates just too full? Should we get some counseling? We have been banging away on each other for perhaps eight to ten weeks, sometimes more intensively than others—and with increasing discomfort for both of us. It's not easy to write about. We don't like to openly admit our inability to control ourselves and our emotions.

Things had so piled up on us that one evening after I went to bed, Martha called our dear friend, Margo Baldwin, a psychologist. Margo insisted on coming to the house, and she and Martha talked it all out together. Margo gave Martha a lot of reassurance, and I felt it too. We are under pressure, and with Margo's help we searched for explanations and understanding of why we were dumping on one another. We shared with one another those aspects of our relationship that had caused us the most trouble—largely that I had nit-picked at Martha, forever pointing out her errors, as I saw them, correcting her actions and speech. Martha had fought back uncharacteristically harshly, attacking me and claiming that I was always blaming her for our wounded relationship. We really had tried hard to avoid doing or saying things we told each other were difficult. It reached the point where we were timid about saying or doing anything for fear of exacerbating an already difficult relationship. We wondered if this was destined to continue and worsen during all my remaining days, and that seemed intolerable. Why did this have to be? Why couldn't we relate with love and caring as we had for so many years? There had to be answers.

Years ago, in connection with the life-insurance business, Martha and I had become acquainted with a theory of social style that defines the characteristics of the driver, the analytical, the amiable, and the expressive personality types. Martha, the consummate amiable, has always behaved as the theory suggests, her principal style being to acquiesce and her back-up style to attack. And I have felt it.

In her wisdom, Martha concluded we needed to know more about *me*—an analytical driver. So we dug out the social psychology we once had used in selling insurance, and there it was, spelled out in crystal-clear terms. My style, according to the theory, is one of avoidance, backed up by being an autocrat. No one can deny my autocratic nature (not even me), but avoidance? Of what? For years, I've had the habit of throwing my hands into the air and with that gesture conveying a sense of "Let's close it down, forget it." Avoidance? You bet! And we discovered several other impressions conveyed by that gesture that are undeniably avoidance.

My avoidance has bothered Martha, and my autocratic style has become even more pronounced as I have sought desperately to nail everything down before I die. I have leaned over backwards to communicate to Martha my confidence in her ability to function successfully after I am gone. I've urged her into areas of future responsibility to allow her to have my assistance while she learns—and I have told the world how well she does. Now I see I've needed to exercise my autocratic nature to assure her my way is the best way. Meanwhile, Martha has needed to be her own person, to assert her own individuality, to shed and shun my influence; therefore, she has intensified

her attack mode to destroy my autocratic style, which is no
longer appropriate.

It was through Chuck's insight that we came to understand what we
were doing. We were both being our basic-personality selves, and
though we have lived together for forty-nine years and have learned
to accommodate one another (and have not threatened one another
for years), we were back at square one, dealing with our basic bare
personalities. We have made beautiful music for all these years—we've
learned how to harmonize—so what happened in the past few
months?

We've been threatened by the progression of the disease, and
we've both been trying unknowingly to show the other one how
things should or will be done. Chuck wants everything lined up so
that I won't have any problems. There's nothing wrong with that
thinking. The only difficulty was that I was intimidated, believing I
couldn't show or wasn't showing him that I was capable of thinking
clearly and would be all right. I thought I was being assertive, when
in fact I wasn't really hearing or rationally discussing situations. I was
too busy trying to show him how independent I was.

We were setting each other up. As soon as we came to this realization, we both felt so good and honestly knew we had grown some
more. I truly feel we were guided by the Holy Spirit, as these things
don't just happen.

AUGUST 19, 1992

Morphine and alcohol are incompatible, so I've stopped drinking. Another concession. The pain-control folks had cautioned
me about drinking and clearly implied that my daily intake of
three to four ounces was a bit much to be mixed with morphine. The morphine, which I know will be increased in dosage
in response to frequent breakthroughs, will become an increasing problem. Even now my confidence in my mental capacities
has waned. I feel empty-headed, forgetful, much less alert. I am
willing to accept this as a trade-off for pain relief. But when it's
exacerbated by booze, I can't accept it. Furthermore I prefer to
stop of my own volition, rather than have the doctors say I
have to. I prefer to be in charge of my own body when possible.

There may be no connection, but last night I had the most
drenching night-sweat of my life—following two extra doses of

narcotics and, as I recall, five or six ounces of Scotch. Martha agreed to eliminate her nightly vodka, saying she drank only to keep me company anyway and reminding me she never drinks when she's alone. So our alcohol consumption will be restricted to a little wine. I wonder how long it will take us to use up our inventory of booze. I'm sure we have enough to float the QE2. And there's no loss without some small gain. What shall I do with the seventy-five dollars a month I've been dropping at the state liquor store? Perhaps we should think about giving it away.

AUGUST 18, 1992

Today we saw Bill B. and Arthur H.–a big day. Bill reported my PSA is 1.6–incredible! He attributes it to Flutamide and used the term "remission." We asked Bill how he defines "escape" and he said he sees it as a precipitous, continuing upward movement of PSA. To my question of "How long thereafter?" he answered, "Twelve months."

Then it was on to Dr. H. My pain has been fairly well controlled with oral morphine, but the jabbing pain has increased. I knew this would mean more morphine, so I complained to him about the side effects I'm already having–memory failure, loss of train of thought, fogginess, and intense itching. We decided he should install an epidural catheter which will enable morphine to be introduced directly into the spinal area. I should get pain relief at one-tenth the oral dosage. I'm having the procedure done tomorrow. I'll try it for a couple of weeks before we make the decision about a permanent catheter.

AUGUST 19, 1992

Catheter installed–twice! After the first installation, the tube became disconnected and contaminated. There was nothing to do but yank it out and start again. Har-de-har!

AUGUST 22, 1992

The pain control is fantastic! No more MS Contin, no need for Percocet, no side effects, and all of this on only 10 percent of the previous dose of morphine. But I just don't feel well. Something is rumbling in my gut. Could it be a new side effect? I sure hope not. I don't want anything to stand in the way of this successful pain control. Please, God, I try not to ask for much for myself, but for this I implore you!

AUGUST 23, 1992

After a miserable night, marked by increasing indigestion, I
vomited copiously. My attitude is terrible. All the nurses seem
to agree this is just a bug, but I'm not convinced.

AUGUST 24, 1992

Maybe it was a bug. I feel better. Over the weekend, though, I
was sure this was the beginning of the end. My emotions were
very fragile. I cried at the slightest provocation. Martha was
brave and supported me where I was. I've never felt closer to
her and never before felt such intensity in her love and support.
It gave me a warm feeling about how we will relate when I do
die.

I wonder why anyone with metastatic prostate cancer would
opt for chemotherapy knowing that at best it *might* reduce
pain—in exchange for intense nausea. We are so grateful to
Arthur and the pain-control service for their willingness to
aggressively pursue the use of narcotics. And now the epidural
catheter is doing the trick. I am literally without pain on 10 percent of the oral dosage of morphine.

I've been advised not to drive while on morphine, not
because I am any more prone to an accident, but because,
should I be hit by an uninsured motorist, his position in court
would possibly be strengthened if he introduced evidence that
I am under constant application of a narcotic, one of whose
side effects is sedation. We have checked—and doubled—our lia-
bility insurance and have told our agent why. As a matter of
practice, however, I don't intend to drive at all if there is any
sense of sedation or sleepiness or if I feel less than in full com-
mand of my mental processes. I'm confident I can discipline
myself in that respect.

SEPTEMBER 22, 1992

It's been almost a month since I have made a journal entry—
and what a month!

On August 24, the home-care nurse came to refill my pump
and discovered that the catheter had worked its way out of the
point of entry into my spine and was pumping morphine exter-
nally. At the hospital a few minutes later, we agreed that it
would be foolish to install another temporary catheter and that
we should move ahead with the placement of a permanent

pump. During the procedure, the pump would be installed below the skin in my left lower abdomen; the internal catheter would end in the subarachnoid space of my spine. This location would enable me to reduce my medication to 1 percent of my previous oral dose of morphine.

> Dr. H. said the operation would take 2½ to 3 hours, because one must be so careful working around the spine. During the time I waited, Betty Vlcek and Margo Baldwin stayed with me. How wonderful to be surrounded by such warm and loving friends! I was fairly calm about it until after 2:00 p.m. By 3:00, I was antsy and uneasy. Chuck, who had epidural anesthesia, was watching the clock and asked Arthur to have someone call me to say everything was all right; things were just taking longer than expected. When Arthur and his nurse came to talk with me, they were still in their scrubs. They filled me in on the complication that had caused the operation to be prolonged.

After everything was in place, Art accidentally severed the catheter, which slithered up my spine like a piece of spaghetti. To his embarrassment and chagrin, Arthur confessed to me the next day the details of his error and how, with the help of the fluoroscope, he had fished out the catheter. The fishing trip extended the surgery an extra one and a half hours. So the operation took four hours, and with preop and postop, poor Martha was there all day.

The surgical problems resulted in an unintended loss of spinal fluid. The next day, the staff kept me flat on my back in an effort to prevent headache and nausea—to no avail. When they carefully assisted me to a sitting position, I was hit across the back of the neck with a pain that felt as if Mickey Mantle had taken a swat at me.

> That morning Chuck gave me his early-morning wake-up call, and he seemed fine. I got my hair done, picked up a present for him, and was at the hospital before noon. We were counting the minutes until he could sit up. About 7:00 p.m., he was allowed up. Wow, what pain he had! He was determined to walk around, thinking that would help him, but he shouldn't have, because he was nauseated.
>
> At 5:30 the next morning he called and told me how sick he had been all night. I immediately got up, ate some breakfast, and dashed to the hospital. When I arrived he was really snowed with morphine to help the nausea. He didn't even know me. When Mary Johnson, a priest from St. Mark's, arrived, he didn't know her either.

It was determined that Chuck's pain arose from the loss of spinal fluid and that he would have the pain and nausea for a week or two. Every time he tried to eat something, the nausea came over him like a wave. He was careful not to lift his head even a little or the pain would return with a vengeance.

A day later, the team came in to regulate the pump. It was fascinating. A wand attached to a portable computer is passed over the pump in Chuck's body. The computer then prints Chuck's name and ID number and tells how much morphine is programmed to be delivered through the catheter, and at what rate and hour. The doctors decided to increase the dose a bit because he was still losing morphine out of the space where the catheter had been placed. Medicine and technology—what a combination!

We were happy Chuck could go home the next day but also apprehensive because he still felt so awful. I kept in touch with the pain-control folks and told them Chuck had slept all day and was still groggy. They said he was probably all right—just feeling the effects of the morphine and the medication for nausea. They called me back the next morning to check on him and reiterated that his nausea was from loss of spinal fluid and that there was nothing he could do but lie flat, drink liquids, and sweat it out. Sweat it out he did. He vomited for five days and five nights. I couldn't even hold his head when he vomited, because just my light touch increased the pain.

After being on his back for a week, he was able to dress and move to the couch, and for the next few days he improved. By the end of two weeks, the headache was gone too. I tried not to be a smothering wife, but I did watch him closely and rejoiced as he improved. As his appetite returned, I tried to prepare foods that appealed to him, so he could put back some of the more than ten pounds he had lost. It did scare me that he had lost so much weight; I felt he was so vulnerable to picking up another bug, and that he didn't need. He finally had the pain regulated, and I so wanted him to have the quality of life we had been told he would have.

This period was most difficult for me emotionally, though I really felt I was being supported by the good Lord. Many times, when I would start to feel overwhelmed, it was as though a reassuring hand were placed on my shoulder and I was steadied; strength poured through me. I can't describe it except to say it was real.

Chuck is like his old self again. He has regained the weight, his step is brisker, his humor has returned, his face is no longer drawn in pain, and we're able to once again enjoy every day. This whole exercise has taught us, once again, that each day stands alone and is precious in and of itself.

SEPTEMBER 23, 1992

Perhaps it's due to the Flutamide and its beneficial effects on my PSA, enabling Bill to refer to my present state as a remission. Perhaps it's the fact that we have surpassed our fondest hopes by beating the statistical odds on metastatic prostate cancer. Whatever the reason, Martha and I have now concluded that a *good day* is *today*. Our focus is on today, and we live only tentatively beyond today. There is something very calming about living with such a revised definition. Somehow the distant days that exist "out there" seem far less important than today, here and now, this minute—the marvelous gift for which our gratitude abounds.

SEPTEMBER 27, 1992

I feel better than I have in months. I'm not sure why it has happened, but it has. Could it be that pain management has restored a quality to my life that leaves much less room for the dwindles, the wobbles, the cave-ins, and the jabs?

Arthur says 95 percent of cancer pain can be successfully managed during the natural course of the disease, but that only 30 percent of cancer patients are receiving such pain-control therapy. Arthur wants to get out into the community and promote awareness of the possibilities existing for people with chronic pain. Martha and I are trying to assist him.

OCTOBER 24, 1992

What a roller-coaster month! Maybe this is what we're going to experience more and more.

After I had written that Chuck was like his old self again and after we had spent a wonderful weekend with his sister, Pauly, and her husband, Jim, Chuck came down with a bug and was one sick fellow. It started with a terrific headache and stiff neck. Since those were the same symptoms he had experienced while he was recovering from the loss of spinal fluid, we felt that maybe all the fluid hadn't been replaced yet. After a couple of miserable days, we called Dr. H., who said Chuck probably needed to have the amount of morphine reduced. Since he was no longer losing medication from the catheter, all the morphine—more than he needed—was going directly to the spine. We immediately went to the hospital, Chuck lying down all the way. A wheelchair was waiting for us, which was a good thing; he was really wiped out.

In addition to turning back the pump, the doctors discovered Chuck had a slight fever. They did some blood work to see if there was infection around the catheter. We sure didn't want that to happen. The staff felt he simply had some kind of virus, so home we came. Chuck fell into bed. His head and neck were so painful. His temperature went up and down, never higher than 100.6°. Arthur called and told us the blood tests were normal, so there was no infection from the operation. He also felt Chuck should see Dr. Cindi, so we went straight to her office. We stayed two and a half hours, as she went over him with a fine-tooth comb. She was quite concerned about the possibility of spinal meningitis.

For the next four days, we waited to see if the cultures would grow and indicate a bacterial infection anywhere. Fortunately nothing showed up, and his temperature came down. He slowly regained his strength, and finally, after a week or so in bed, he got up and dressed. He was terribly weak and discouraged, though. We know that his underlying disease makes him vulnerable to bugs, and that anyone who stays in bed for a week is weak and tired, but Chuck felt and looked so frail and worn out.

The doctors, who kept in close touch with us, decided the best plan of attack was to cancel all plans for the next two weeks to let Chuck get himself built back up. We had planned on several out-of-town guests, whom we had to call and cancel. Everyone understood, but it was still hard to do. It's been well worth it, though, as Chuck is feeling stronger. In fact, we started walking again this week. Today we did about fifty minutes, and that's great. Way back at the beginning of his illness, Bob told us to keep walking, and we're both sure it was one of the best prescriptions Chuck has had. The disease makes him weak anyway, but when he loses muscle tone in his back and legs, the weakness is even more pronounced.

One of my idiosyncrasies is to do well during a crisis, but when the danger is past, I become a zombie and am emotionally fragile. Through the past six weeks I've been very proud of myself, but earlier this week I fell apart. All of a sudden I was teary, my stomach was tied in knots, and my frame of mind was miserable. One of the hardest things to deal with was walking by myself. For more than eight years Chuck and I have walked every day, and during those three-to-four-mile walks, we've done lots of talking. We've discussed books, religion, politics, differences, all kinds of topics. Walking for us isn't exercise; it's an experience that's most precious. When I walk alone, I miss my buddy, and at times my anticipatory grief overwhelms me.

This latest episode shows me I'm still working on acceptance—not the acceptance of Chuck's cancer; that happened long ago. But I realize I haven't accepted the fact that his strength doesn't come back to where it was when he has a setback. I know that his underlying cancer, which causes him weakness, isn't going to stop while he deals with a virus, which also results in weakness. Yet when the bug is gone, I want him restored to where he was before. In reality, I haven't accepted the fact that Chuck is going to grow weaker and weaker, and when he has a bout that brings on weakness, I'm devastated. I want to push that away and not think about it. Acceptance is such a simple word, but acceptance isn't easy and has to be won over and over again.

It was so good to be in church with Chuck this morning. It took a lot of energy from him, but it added more from the love that was given to him.

NOVEMBER 3, 1992

My PSA is 0.7. It has never been that low, even after my original surgery and orchiectomy. Hallelujah! Bill says current statistics reveal that 80 percent of patients who benefit from Flutamide so many months after orchiectory are still alive two years after beginning the medication. He's increasingly confident I'll be here to celebrate our fiftieth wedding anniversary next year. On the other side of the coin, he has no explanation for my persistent weakness and fatigue. He says it is surely related to my disease, and given all I've been through this year, the cumulative effects are hard to rebuild from. He says, however, that my former strength should return.

Patients had better learn that medicine is more an art than a science and that physicians operate only from informed opinion and judgment.

> The two additional years Bill mentioned made my heart sing. I know the cancer isn't gone and, as Bill said, the weakness and fatigue are part of the disease, but he feels Chuck is regaining a lot of the strength he lost when he had the pump installed and when he suffered the two bouts of illness. As I think of it, I realize he has gained a good deal of strength in just the last two weeks. I know he can't get back to where he was three years ago—or even a year ago—but I do

think he'll develop enough strength to go out to breakfast and enjoy being with friends again.

It's strange to feel contradictory. I'm thrilled beyond words with the PSA and the fact that the disease has slowed down, but I also feel cautious, almost afraid to feel so good. One thing's for sure: I'm grateful for all the advancements that have been made, grateful for the aggressive treatment, and grateful for this anniversary, because we now know we have a good chance of celebrating the next one as well.

NOVEMBER 17, 1992

A few days ago, I felt almost normal. My fatigue and weakness dissipated to a degree for which I had only hoped—and that hope had been waning. It was the perfect time for it to happen. On Friday we entertained for the first time since September, and on Saturday we went out to dinner at the Vlceks. On Sunday I read the Scripture at church, we attended an open house, and then we called on a woman who had recently lost her husband.

It's encouraging to know such days of restored energy are possible and will occur again, in spite of the fact that the past two days have seen a return to fatigue and weakness.

Chuck had to pay a price for all this activity. He is fatigued, and his energy level is down. On the positive side, however, we're pleased that his energy level rises as well as falls. The key is to try not to pile so much into our schedule. Sometimes, no matter what we do, however, activities do pile up. We both wish Chuck's energy would stay at a single level, but we're recognizing that this isn't the nature of cancer.

As for me, I've been struggling the last few days, and I've been trying to figure out why. Last Saturday I came apart over a simple financial transaction that didn't take more than five minutes to do. In my gut, however, I didn't want to do anything more than curl up with a book. I had had a busy week, doing things I enjoy. I was tired emotionally and physically; the events of September and October finally caught up with me; and the financial transaction pointed out to me that I was now in charge of this aspect of our lives—and I didn't like the reason.

Chuck told me I needed to slow down and be good to myself. Unfortunately, I felt picked on and said so, which didn't make Chuck very happy and made me terribly sorry I'd said anything.

DECEMBER 5, 1992

Our forty-ninth anniversary was glorious! We started the weekend celebration by going out to breakfast on Friday at the Hyatt on Capitol Square. We sat there for two and a half hours, enjoying each other's company, eating delicious fruit and pastries, and drinking gallons of coffee. After that we drove to Engle's Wholesale Florist, there to pick up the forty-nine roses symbolizing our forty-nine years. Chuck started this custom forty-nine years ago with one rose. How precious each of those roses is!

The next day, on our anniversary, we exchanged special letters to one another and spent a lovely day just being together. In the evening we were treated to a gourmet catered meal from Tom, Carol, Nicole, and Max. The table was set with our crystal, silver, and china, and at 6:00 p.m., the doorbell rang, announcing the arrival of our meal. We started with a Caesar salad and smoked salmon, followed by rib eye of veal topped with pieces of lobster, herbed linguini, and six spears of fresh, tender asparagus. With this we had dinner rolls and a bottle of Merlot. The caterer then arranged our dessert on a dessert plate: a strawberry tart, cheese cake, a raspberry tart in a chocolate wafer shell, a raspberry-and-strawberry-filled pastry, and an upside-down peach half, arranged in a fan shape. On each was a dollop of whipping cream.

The caterer left as we were beginning our main course, so we were there alone in the candlelight, eating like royalty, talking and reminiscing. Before dinner, as we drank some wine, we looked at our wedding pictures, reread our service, and relived some precious memories. How fortunate we have been—and are!

JANUARY 1, 1993

New Year's Day has always been my favorite holiday. It is so totally a new beginning. But today New Year's Day is even more special. Two years ago Stan predicted six to twelve months more of good days. But here I am in 1993, in remission, with a strong possibility we'll celebrate Martha's seventieth birthday and our fiftieth anniversary this year *together!* What a blessing! What a gift! Thanks be to God!

JANUARY 4, 1993

Martha and I have been thinking deeply about healing. Healing is not *cure,* but *reconciliation*—the restoration of wholeness. Healing can occur even among the darkest circumstances, because healing comes from God's peace.

JANUARY 5, 1993

We had a glorious Christmas! The joy of being with Karen and her family was superb. Tom, Carol, and Max came up from Washington, so we were all together except for Nicole, who was with her mother. This was the first time we'd been to Boston for Christmas since 1986. My mother fell and broke her hip in 1988, when we were supposed to be there. 1989 was Tom's year to have Christmas, so we were there. In 1990, Karen's year, I had the brain surgery, and in 1991 we were at Tom's again. We were eagerly looking forward to being at Karen's and didn't want anything to mar the occasion this year. We were all a little uptight, but we became more confident as we got closer to the day.

Chuck did so well. He took care of himself by staying around the house rather than going out on errands and using energy he didn't need to expend. He never had to withdraw; he never looked strained; and he was able to stay up a couple of hours past his usual bedtime. He thoroughly enjoyed having the chance to visit individually with Brian and Colby, and there wasn't a minute he wasn't full of animation. It was wonderful to see, and I was more grateful than I can express in words. It was a special Christmas gift for all of us.

JANUARY 12, 1993

It has taken me since December 26 to write this, because it is unlike me to have an experience like the one I'm about to relate. It has never happened to me before, and when others have revealed such experiences, I've attempted to understand, but believed they were describing dreams, hallucinations, or illusions. I couldn't even discuss this with Martha—and we tell each other everything—until I had time to reflect on it.

We were in Boston, and it was nearly time to get up. I was lying quietly, waiting for Martha to waken. I was fully awake, thinking about the applications of cellular technology I'd discussed with Tom and Doug the night before. Suddenly, a strong voice called my name. And then after a short pause, somewhat more quietly it said, "We are ready for you."

Who was that? I asked myself. Was it God? Jesus? The Holy Spirit? I was awestruck, but there was no sense of doubt in my mind, not at all. It was real. When we returned to our church in Columbus, Melody preached on angels, to whom she referred as "messengers." That was enough for me. It was a messenger, and I'll just have to leave it at that. It is more than I can find word to express, let alone explain. I know unequivocally that the messenger said what I heard. There may also have been more—something about calling me—but the voice became faint. I do think there was some reference to my being called to come at some unspecified time.

I've told this only to Martha and Melody, although I may share it with Tom and Karen at the appropriate time. It's interesting that both Melody and Martha asked me how I felt about it. I told them I felt:

- an inability to explain it and an awareness of how quickly and easily I have "explained" the experiences of others;
- a deep sense of peace and well-being;
- a sense of limbo between my current status of remission and the inevitable; and
- a reminder of the great and exciting journey I'm facing and the sadness and hurt it will bring to my family.

I felt good about it, reassured, healed, whole, filled with God's peace, and perhaps a little apprehensive, but then, it's a human propensity to feel anxious about the unknown.

> When Chuck told me what had happened, I was quiet for a moment to check my own feelings. I felt calm, because I knew Chuck wasn't alone; he wasn't going down his path by himself. I don't know whether "We're ready" means days, weeks, or months, but knowing Chuck will never be alone is comforting to me.

JANUARY 10, 1993

> Being caught unawares is surprising, and it happened to me twice this week. First, when we were having breakfast with Melody, I heard Chuck ask her if she would perform his service of memory and preach the homily while Michael celebrated the Eucharist. That's fine with me, but I wasn't expecting to hear it right now. We both love Melody, and she and Chuck are very close. Nonetheless I was taken completely off-guard.
>
> The other surprise happened tonight when we were talking with Karen. Chuck told her he was doing OK but wondered if he could wait to see Dr. H. before having his pain pump turned up. I was floored, because I had thought he was doing as well as he had in Boston, and I had been so thrilled. I knew he still had pain when he moved or bent over; I knew he got stabbed every now and then; I knew he was occasionally wiped out. But it didn't seem as bad as it

had before Christmas, when he looked so drawn and tired. Maybe my eagerness to have him feeling better affected my observations. Whatever the reason, I was surprised.

FEBRUARY 1, 1993

Chuck and I have talked about not going to Florida. He knows that I love to travel; I know that at this time he's more comfortable here at home. I really don't want to go unless he's comfortable about doing it. This is a time when we want to do things that are easy and happy for us both, a time to do what we can do and not to be unhappy about what we can't.

We also discussed whether I should go to the funeral home and take care of the arrangements now. I said no, since I believe this is something I need to do with the children. We talked about the memorial service, and I asked to see what he had written and what some of his ideas were. I firmly believe a memorial service should be a combination of the deceased's ideas and those of the survivors. I'm so glad we can and did talk about this. It's not crepe-hanging; it's being real, and it helps us cope.

It wasn't a happy time, and I'm filled with sad thoughts, but I'm still ready to say that today was a good day. It's still amazing to me that, with all the sadness, I can feel such peace.

FEBRUARY 3, 1993

Yesterday was a big day. We found out that Chuck's PSA had risen since October, which means his remission is over. It was a hard time for me. I had been scared about the report, because I knew Chuck was having more breakthroughs. At first, his PSA of 1.3 didn't seem like much, but Bill said it was a 10 percent upward shift and was significant. He also said that when the PSA was going down, he had to believe the tumors were shrinking. Since it's going up, he now has to believe they're growing.

After our doctor visit, I just felt numb all over. I heard and knew what was said, I talked with the kids, Chuck and I talked, but my mind just didn't want to connect with the idea of his remission being over. I talked with several friends who wanted to know how we had come out at the doctor's, and we had some friends in for a short happy hour, dinner, and conversation. All the while, I felt as if I were playing a role. No one knew how heavy my heart was.

Today it seems as if the motor inside me is running at full speed. Physically I'm moving more slowly. Things I read don't stick in my mind, the bliss of cooking takes longer, I'm preoccupied. I talked with Melody this morning and told her about my feelings of role-playing. She told me I'll play lots of roles during this stressful time, but suggested that I remember that those roles are what keep me in touch with the rest of life around me. I had never thought of that. Life does go on, in spite of hurts and sorrows.

February 21, 1993

Today my heart and mind are full of the blessings of snuggling. Since Chuck goes to bed long before I do, I climb into bed with him and snuggle for between thirty minutes and an hour. This is a special time for us. We haven't been able to have sex for four years. We have both missed this part of our marriage, as the sexual part was another dimension of expressing our love. Snuggling is the next best thing, and we cherish each moment in each other's arms. There's nothing like feeling the warmth of my lover beside me, to be enveloped by his arms, to have his lips find mine. We may talk or watch television or just lie quietly and savor the experience. It is a ritual that is precious, and we both look forward to it.

March 19, 1993

Chuck had his pain pump turned up last week, and what a difference it's made! This has been a good week, filled with activity. We were blessed with a visit from our son-in-law Sunday afternoon and evening, and on Monday Tom came for an overnight. On Tuesday we were up early to take Tom to the airport, and at noon we left for the theater to see *Fidelio*. It was marvelous, but it's a long opera, and it was 5:00 p.m. before we got home. On Thursday we were gone all afternoon, and today we were out all morning.

Chuck has been able to do all this because of the pain pump. It really shows how uncontrolled pain can eat a person up. The pump may not change the course of the disease, but it certainly does make for good days; it doesn't deter the tumors, but it does add quality to life.

March 25, 1993

Our rector, Michael Jupin, spent three hours with us the other afternoon, and it was a beautiful and fulfilling experience. Michael knows how close Chuck and I are, and he has been experiencing us as we deal with Chuck's illness and has said he would like to share our journey with us.

We told Michael we are peaceful, but sad. He asked what we meant by sadness, and we both remarked about separation and the different paths we are following. The conversation helped bring us to an understanding of the close relationship between joy and pain. Chuck and I can be so happy doing something together, and then, zowie, the realization comes that someday we won't be doing it. That brings pain. They are truly bittersweet moments.

MARCH 30, 1993

Chuck has bronchitis, and it has laid him low. We've been discussing how we are going to deal with out-of-town relatives and friends who want to come to see us this summer. Chuck has little energy now. What's it going to be like when his energy level is nil? We think we need to create some boundaries—nothing set in stone, but boundaries.

I have to take care of myself physically, emotionally, and spiritually. My spiritual life sustains me. I want to see family and friends, but as Chuck gets worse, my stress will increase, and a weekend of guests may be more than I can tolerate. I think it only fair we tell out-of-towners we must coordinate visits, because Chuck can't handle back-to-back visitors. And Tom and Karen take precedence over all others.

After he spent a miserable night coughing, Chuck told me that if this illness progresses to pneumonia, we should just let it take its course, as it would alleviate a lot of further suffering. I was speechless. We both agreed to no heroics, but I hadn't thought of fighting pneumonia as heroics.

On my walk, I asked God for guidance, since I couldn't get my mind to deal with the issue. I knew Chuck and I had a lot more talking to do. I also felt that we required more input from his doctors and that I needed Michael's and Melody's support. Later in the morning, Chuck was feeling better, his temperature was coming down, and we continued our discussion. We agreed he was being a little premature, but it had been a good exercise for us to think about. If some unexpected complication should arise and we have to make the heroics decision, we'll have an understanding from which to work.

We both agree longevity is not important; quality is.

APRIL 3, 1993

One part of this scenario I have not looked forward to is the moment Chuck gives some of his precious mementos to the children and grandchildren. I want them to have these possessions, but knowing

Chuck will give them up near the end of his life and knowing how emotional it will be for him, for me, and for them has made it a difficult idea. As I walked this morning, I asked God to give me the strength I'll need to face that moment.

This afternoon, Chuck told me he has changed his mind about giving the kids his special things; he wants me to do it immediately after it's all over. He felt his doing it would be too hard on all of us. I promised him I would see that all parties receive their items before they go home. I am relieved, and though it will be hard, it will also be an honor to do it for Chuck.

APRIL 11, 1993

Easter. What a glorious day! A friend from out of town called and said she imagined this wasn't a happy Easter for us. I said it was a wonderful Easter. Easter is a symbol of eternal life. Faith doesn't take away hurt or pain, but it does give me the strength to face them, and it gives me an inner peace that can't be denied.

When we had Chuck's pain pump turned up this week, we had the chance to talk with Dr. H. for an hour. We told him about the bronchitis and said that Chuck has had four bouts with viruses since last fall. Arthur reminded us that Chuck's immune system isn't as strong as it once was. Chuck then told him how he and I had wrestled with the pneumonia question; he wanted to know what other complications could cause his death. Art replied, "Kidney failure, spinal fractures that cause excruciating pain, and other illnesses caused by the breakdown of the immune system." He also said Chuck could just waste away.

None of this is happy to think about. It's apparent now that we need to think more about heroics and their use in common disorders, such as kidney problems. We've always said we wanted no heroics if it meant life as a vegetable, but we hadn't thought about heroics being antibiotics or dialysis. These are hard choices, and I don't believe they can be made ahead of time, but it's something to think about and have some mutual understanding about. Changes can happen so quickly in advanced cancer.

APRIL 19, 1993

Chuck has had to start using a cane for support. When Arthur learned Chuck was stumbling more and having trouble catching himself if he started to fall, he said it was time for a cane. This, of course, did not please Chuck. On my suggestion, he called the health-care center, and the physical therapist showed him how to use a cane properly. She determined the proper height for it. The therapist performed some tests to evaluate Chuck's ability to respond to nerve impulses from his legs. We know from the last CT scan that there are tumors impinging on his spinal nerves. Fortunately, they won't cause paralysis, but they are causing numbness in his extremities.

We learned a lot about balance and how our bodies accommodate us to maintain our balance. Chuck has been using the cane more regularly now and really notices how much more secure he feels with it. I'm so proud of him; it was not an easy thing for him to accept. I've told him he looks quite debonair, which is true, but that doesn't make it any easier.

Chuck's weakness and fatigue are his main problems, since we mercifully have the pain under control. The poor guy is still tired even after he's been in bed for ten or eleven hours. That's got to be a miserable feeling, but he gets up, dresses, and helps me fix breakfast. Sometimes he fixes it himself while I do the laundry or finish my morning walk. His appetite is good, for which I'm grateful, and we have a most enjoyable breakfast with our cereal and homemade breads.

There are times we go out to breakfast with friends, and that's fun. The key to Chuck's getting some energy in the morning is to ply him with coffee. When we're out, he almost drinks the restaurant dry, while at home he retires to his lounge chair with his coffee.

These are still good days, and we'll take them all, but they are trying days. There is no way to predict when Chuck's energy will leave him, so we both try to be flexible. When the starch comes out of him, it's gone. It's embarrassing for him to be talking with someone when he comes unplugged. He so wants to be his own vibrant self, and until the fatigue hits, he is.

We've always enjoyed taking our late afternoon baths, getting into our robes, having happy hour while we read or talk, and then having dinner. By the time dinner is over, Chuck is more than ready for bed. It's really painful for him to stay awake, and to clear the table takes away any energy he has left. When he hits the bed, he groans with pleasure at being tucked into his little cocoon. I crawl in beside him to snuggle for about an hour, and then I kiss him goodnight and go into the den to read, write, or talk on the phone.

I can't believe that after all these years I'm still working on acceptance. I accept the cancer, I accept the concessions, I accept the changes in our lives, but I'm not accepting Chuck's decline very well.

I'm apprehensive about the near term and most uneasy about the future. Today, as I talked with Melody, I knew I hadn't really accepted the progression of Chuck's disease. I want to say, "Stop! This can't be happening." But it is.

MAY 9, 1993

This month has been difficult. The cancer is gaining on Chuck. His pain is 90 percent controlled by the pump, but when a breakthrough comes, it's as though someone is stabbing him with a knife. Dr. H. has him on a couple of medications for the breakthrough pain, the first being liquid morphine, but that gave him the old side effects of lost memory and fuzziness in the head, plus intense itching. Switching to Dilaudid helped until last week, when he had so much breakthrough, the Dilaudid dose caused the same side effects. Fortunately, the stabbing pain subsided, and Arthur turned up the pump. Chuck would really like to be able to live with only the morphine from the pump, and so far that's been possible.

While all this has been going on, I've had days where I can't seem to slow my body down. I have to keep moving. It's almost as though if I keep moving, I won't think about the situation, but of course that's not true. Other times I'm just generally anxious. Once I admit my feelings and let myself cry, I settle down.

One of the greatest helps remains prayer–not "gimme" praying, which doesn't do any good. When I can be quiet and let God come in, I realize that all I can do for Chuck is to be beside him, supporting him and loving him.

Today at our Sunday morning class at church, the speaker, Sister Maxine Shonk, talked about what Mary has meant in her life. Mary, of course, plays a more prominent role in the Roman Catholic church than in Protestant churches, so all of us in the class started at a different point from Sister Maxine. As she talked about the probable struggle Mary had experienced when she was called to be the mother of Christ and later while watching her Son be crucified, Sister Maxine helped me understand more fully Mary's great faith and the strength that came from that faith. I have always known that God gives strength and that His grace is present all the time. During these years, Chuck and I have grown both in love and faith, and we both feel the "peace that passes all understanding." But it's a lot easier when I let go and let God work in my life.

JUNE 17, 1993

We had two very good weeks while we visited the kids. We first went to Tom's in Washington and then on to Boston to see Karen and to be present for Colby's graduation.

Tom and Carol were wonderful and turned their schedules around so Tom was home in time for an early dinner. During the day, Chuck had time to read and relax, and that was good. Tom had tickets for *Guys and Dolls,* and Chuck felt up to going, so that was fun. The rest of the time there was good conversation, which is always stimulating. All in all, Chuck did very well, with no added pain or fatigue.

In Boston, we attended all the graduation festivities—seven more days of back-to-back activities. Karen had borrowed a recliner chair that was set up in the family room, and there Chuck reigned, as everything at Karen's home was centered around that room.

Those two weeks were a bit of serendipity, and my heart danced with joy. The entire experience was beyond my wildest hopes and dreams.

JULY 11, 1993

Two nights ago I had three powerful dreams which awakened me each time with a feeling of anxiety. Each time, I looked over and touched Chuck to make sure he was still there. I recorded only one of the dreams, because their themes were all the same; only the setting differed.

I was going down a long hall with Chuck; we turned and entered a room. As I tried to shut the door, I saw it wouldn't close. I peered out the door, and a smiling figure who was going down the hall turned back. There was also a woman named Marie in the hall. I called to her to have her distract the figure so that I could shut the door. As I tried again to close it, the figure got her foot in the door. I couldn't shut it. I was frantic, and at the moment I wakened with my heart beating wildly. Two more similar dreams followed. Obviously, they all had to do with losing Chuck. It became clear that I haven't been doing my homework about Chuck's death. Whenever I start to really think about it, I repress it, saying these are good days, and I don't want to ruin them with worry about the future.

These dreams flooded my mind all day, and I was completely preoccupied about their meaning. When I told Margo about them, she told me my subconscious is crying out, trying to tell me to deal with the reality of Chuck's death. She asked me to come and see her so we could talk.

I told Margo about the concern I have always had about being left alone; I told her it took me two years to get over Mother's death, and I know it will be even harder with Chuck. Margo and I talked about my letting go, and about the necessity for Chuck to see and know that I'm OK and not desperately hanging on to him. Then I told her about my talking to and encouraging Mother to breathe and about bringing her back when she was taken off the ventilator, and how afterwards she had asked me why she was still alive. It was after that that I had given her permission to die. So I knew what Margo was saying.

Margo asked me some more about the figure I'd seen in my dream. She asked me what I'd say to it if I opened the door and spoke to her. That was hard for me to decide, but I said, "Please don't take him now. I'm not ready."

At that point I mentioned Chuck's experience with the voice he heard in Boston. I don't usually go around sharing Chuck's experiences, but this seemed appropriate, and for the first time I saw the connection between my dream and Chuck's voice. I knew I didn't want my dream figure or his voice to have him yet. All the while I was talking to Margo, my tears were falling. I know I haven't been dealing with the actuality of Chuck's death. My dreams are my body telling me I need to talk about my fears and about what I think the future will bring. I need to share this with Chuck. He and I have always shared everything, but I confessed to Margo that I felt guilty about my fears and anxieties; after all, I have so much to be grateful for. Margo gently reminded me that I listen to Chuck's fears and anxieties and that I'd feel cheated if he didn't share them with me. Wouldn't Chuck feel cheated if I didn't share mine with him? Oh, my, I wouldn't want Chuck to feel cheated, and I now see that working through my thoughts and fears with him won't take away the basic problem, but it will soften the pain. He is my buddy, my lover, and my best friend.

I didn't bother to put on any eye makeup this morning, as I knew I'd be sharing all this with Chuck as we walked. I was right. The tears flowed, and Chuck was most understanding. He knew I'd been working on something because it had been hard for him to communicate with me. Finally, my mind was really dealing with my needs. It's as though the dam has broken. Another milestone is passed. Thank you, God, for friends like Margo.

JULY 21, 1993

Chuck's pain pump has been such a wonderful help. For the past ten months, we've been living in a span of time filled with good days. Since May 5, it has been set up five or six times and has given Chuck a quality of life he certainly wouldn't have had without it.

Yesterday, we spent over two hours at the James seeing Arthur and Bill. Chuck's pump has now been set 100 percent higher than what it was in May. His PSA has increased significantly over the past two months, and Bill says the tumors are growing. He will never be pinned down to any timetable, but he says Chuck is on the downhill track. As Bill talked about the possibilities–broken bones, or a collapsing spine because of the cancer eating away at the bones, or the cancer attacking the kidney, liver, or lungs–I thought what a choice it was. He could have horrible pain from bone involvement or be struck with an acute situation in his soft tissues. No matter what, we heard loud and clear that the end is coming.

Both doctors were so caring, and both said to call them anytime. Bill, in particular, said he wants to keep in close touch with Chuck, so we'll see him in two months, unless we need to be there sooner.

AUGUST 4, 1993

We have repeatedly noticed the name of Patrice Rancour in publications from the James. As a clinical nurse-specialist, she has written about her counseling work with patients at the hospital and their families. In a recent article, she said, "It is very important to let people know that even if curing the physical disease isn't possible, healing their lives is." That did it. We had to meet Patrice.

I called, and this morning Martha and I spent an hour with her. She offered some new and fascinating insights, but mostly she affirmed us, our thinking, and our attitudes. It was most satisfying, almost as if we were singing the same song. We told her we wanted to give away what we've discovered, and she wants to be a bridge between us and others–an exciting prospect.

From Patrice's office, we went to the pain-control center to have my pump filled and the dosage increased. I'm now taking 17 mg per day, as opposed to 7 mg when I began in May. It's a great device that surely has added to the quality of my life, but it's now evident that all the professionals acknowledge I'm on the way out.

AUGUST 6, 1993

A couple of days ago, it got pretty funny around here. I woke at 3:00 a.m. to the sound of a beeper, rather faint, but loud enough to waken me. Thinking it was from the microwave, I got out of bed and headed toward the kitchen. Passing the TV, I heard the beep again and determined that it was from the cable TV control box. Deciding that 3:00 a.m. was no time to call the cable company, I returned to bed.

As I sat on the edge of the bed, I heard the beep again. "Aha," I thought, "a malfunction of the hot-water system that flows through the radiator." But surely the hot water wasn't activated at that hour. So I listened, and, sure enough, it beeped again. I decided I'd report the problem to maintenance in the morning.

I decided to make a trip to the bathroom, and there I was greeted by a beeping toilet. Finally, it got through my dull head that it was Ole Dad who was beeping. I journeyed to the den where I found the manual for the pump, which instructed me to call my doctor immediately. That seemed a little urgent, so I decided to keep my scheduled appointment for a refill in seven hours. In case the beep meant absolute empty, I took an oral morphine when I got up.

At my appointment it was found that there was a very small amount left in the pump. I'd best not push it too far when the beeper sounds.

At breakfast with friends the following day, I recounted this tale. One of the party asked what the beep sounded like. I said she would have to hear it. So, in front of everyone in the restaurant, I trekked over to her side of the table. She put her ear to my abdomen. "I heard it," she said. Her husband indicated that he could get along without ever hearing my beeper. We didn't interview any of those at nearby tables.

AUGUST 5, 1993

Chuck has had two back-to-back weeks of fatigue, weakness, and pain. In the past there has usually been a respite of a day or two, but these two weeks haven't brought such a respite. The pain is controlled, but now it is always with him. He is able to get relief by sitting in his recliner or changing position, but it's still there. The jabbing pain continues to come unexpectedly, whether he is active or sitting quietly.

As we were walking, I asked him how all this made him feel. He paused for a couple of minutes and said he didn't know how to say it without hurting me, but he was impatient to get on with the dying and to get it over with.

I understood his answer. I've watched how he stumbles when he's walking; I've seen how he stops part way up a small hill, not to catch his breath, but to gather energy. We both laughed the other morning when he was shuffling along, and we remembered how we'd see other people walking the way he is and think, Oh, those poor souls. Now we're the poor souls. We can laugh about it, thank goodness, but it still hurts.

AUGUST 10, 1993

When people ask, "How are you?" they seem to want no more than a superficial positive response. Now, as an honest and forthright answer involves references to my death, it becomes a dilemma to know how to respond, and it's tempting to give a general, off-the-cuff rejoinder. I told Martha I wished people wouldn't ask the question at all, but I know that other's silence–their not asking–leaves me isolated.

No sooner had we had this conversation than I was put to the ultimate test. A friend asked, "So how does it feel to know you're dying?" Because we were in a restaurant, I refrained from embracing her. Instead I thanked her for her question and commented that no one else had had the courage to put it to me so directly. I quietly and, I hope, sensitively revealed my sense of peace, healing, and anticipation, and I talked about my sadness as I contemplate the end of a wonderful life with Martha. Martha talked about her sadness, her absence of peace and healing, and her confidence that those feelings will ultimately come to her after I have gone and she has grieved. It was a rich, rewarding experience for us both, and so timely.

AUGUST 25, 1993

"Do you have a feeling of abandonment?" Patrice asked Martha. To Martha's negative response, she said, "Perhaps you will as time passes." She then explained her question. "As Chuck approaches his time of death, his attention will focus on the work of dying, which will increasingly exclude the people and circumstances surrounding him." She equated it to the work of birthing, when the mother's focus narrows so as to exclude everything and everyone around her.

Abandonment. A terribly harsh word that connotes being left alone to shift for oneself. I think it's an apt word to describe the feelings of the survivor who experiences emptiness, isolation, helplessness, and powerlessness. For Martha, the word is too harsh. She prefers *separation,* but separation to me is like going overseas, implying a temporary status—not enough.

Martha points to things I have arranged for her—home, finances, roots—that will abide, lingering and lasting memories that will conjure up a sense of continuing relationship, and she points to our faith that we will be together again.

> To me abandonment is an act that has been done to one. Chuck is not abandoning me. He is going to die, to leave me. I'm going to feel alone but not abandoned. I've always said that if I were the survivor, I'd gladly pay the price of aloneness for all the love and togetherness we've shared. As Patrice says, the golden thread that runs between our hearts will never be broken. I know there will be times—there have been some already—when Chuck will be preoccupied with his dying, and I will feel separated, but I am aware of and will understand my loneliness. How could it be otherwise when for fifty years, I've had my buddy, my lover, my Chuck at my side, sharing everything?

SEPTEMBER 7, 1993

A year ago, I was in pretty bad shape and, I was convinced, going downhill. My pain pump had just been installed, and I was trying to overcome the effects of the loss of spinal fluid due to surgery. Further problems made me terribly ill. It was not more than mildly encouraging to me that Flutamide had driven my PSA down from 11.5 to 1.6. I just didn't believe it. So many things had combined to make me feel so bad, I was pretty sure I was on my way out.

A year later, I'm certain the combined effects of Flutamide and the application of morphine via the pain pump have served to give me another year, a mighty long respite by any-one's calculation, and for that gift we are abundantly grateful.

Now we are wondering again. We know the remission ended soon after the dawn of 1993, and since then nothing has been done to attempt any heroics. It used to be that with the help of this journal, we were able to observe change, but only over a period of months. Now we note change in periods as short as a few days. For example:

- Until the past few days, I could negotiate a hill as we walked, without having to stop and gather strength. Now I find myself pausing two or three times.
- Increasing the dosage on my pain pump used to result in my being essentially pain-free for about two weeks. This time, in spite of having it set up 24 percent, I've experienced no pain-free days, and both the jabs and the aches have been more intense and unremitting. I simply can't imagine what the pain would be like without this morphine and the pump, or what it would be like to have to consume ten times my present dose if I had to take it orally, as I calculate it would require seventy MS Contin at 30 mg each over a twenty-four-hour period. I'd be out cold or would have long since died from the ravages of pain.
- My wobbles are more pronounced than in the recent past. I lose my balance—often when walking, sometimes when standing still. A few weeks ago my cane was helpful. Now it's a necessity.
- As each week passes, I spend more and more time in my recliner chair.
- People who once rushed to tell me how good I look are becoming more scarce, while more people say nothing at all to me but quietly tell Martha that I seem to be slipping.

Martha's seventieth birthday is two days hence, and it's one of the key days to which we've pointed. We thank God we have made that big day together.

SEPTEMBER 14, 1993

Tom and Karen were here for Martha's birthday. What a superb visit! It was the first time the four of us had been together alone for more than twenty-five years. They pulled out all the stops, and we all experienced a tremendous high.

For some time I've been considering my desire to give each of our kids, their spouses, and their children some of my most precious possessions. When I considered how I might do this, I was aware it would be a profoundly emotional experience for us all, and I wasn't sure that I could do it or that I wanted to do it to them. As a matter of fact, at one point I told Martha I didn't think I could go through with it and asked her to make the gifts for me after I was gone. As one might expect, she readily agreed, but I didn't feel right about it. They were my gifts, and the presentations were my responsibility. It hadn't occurred to me to make the gifts to Tom and Karen yet, but in church on Sunday morning, it came to me that this was the time—a moment of supreme joy and happiness—and that any later date was destined to produce a darker climate.

So later, around the coffee table, I told them of my wishes, and with a great outpouring of love and emotion, I first removed my cross from my own neck and placed it around Karen's. Then I rose to pick up *Boy* from his position of prominence in our living room and placed him in Tom's lap.

Making these gifts left me with two enormous holes in my life, but I wanted Tom and Karen to have them as a token of love. Later I wondered where *Boy* and the cross and necklace might be in another fifty or one hundred years, and I hoped these gifts might be the beginning of a lasting tradition, carrying with it all the meaning of the original gifts. Of such traditions are perpetuated the bonds of love so vital to a family's evolution.

SEPTEMBER 19, 1993

One of the blessings of morphine is that Chuck doesn't remember past pain, so it's hard for him to tell the pain-control people what he's going through except in general terms. I tell them of his involuntary exclamations of pain, of his exhaustion when he drops into bed, of his remarking that his legs just "aren't there." If he's not feeling those things when we go to the doctor, he doesn't remember them, and the doctors need to know. This has been difficult for Chuck to grasp, because he's always been in charge of his illness.

Because of the symptoms he's been having, I expected his PSA would be up, and when Bill told us it had doubled in sixty days, I was dismayed, but not surprised. It's a funny contradiction: I don't want to hear about the progression of his illness, yet when I hear it has worsened, I feel that my observations have been confirmed.

We both left the James with the same feelings and have been pondering them. It seems clear everyone is in limbo status, waiting for the other shoe to drop; we all seem to recognize that something's got to give. My PSA is rising rapidly, 117 percent in a short sixty days. Although my morphine dose is radically increased, pain persists, as does my mental confusion. My weakness continues unabated. I am more enervated even in the last few days.

Big things are happening in our lives. I have written my obituary and have withdrawn from planning my memorial service; that's the exclusive right of Martha, Tom, and Karen. We are approaching the fork in the road. The signs are clearly visible now, and the fork may be just around the next bend or over the next rise. The ever-increasing space between us will deny us first our precious ability to touch and share our presence and then finally our sight of each other. This is immensely difficult to contemplate, but we will accept it. This is our commitment to God, to life itself, and to each other.

But it isn't easy.

SEPTEMBER 22, 1993

We talk and talk, sometimes when it feels as if we have little to say. We often express our most private and personal thoughts, even those that are darkest. Nothing is barred, no words avoided, nothing buried. We share our hopes and uncertainties; we acknowledge them to one another, examine them, and often arrive at welcome conclusions. It's amazing how often we discover that we're having similar thoughts at the same time. We characterize our nearly fifty years of marriage as an experience in personal growth, and we attribute this to our openness and sharing. It is little wonder these are such happy days.

SEPTEMBER 25, 1993

To someone's inquiry concerning my willingness to participate in a project, I heard myself respond, "I really am too busy." Busy? I have lots of time, in spite of our current style of defensive living. But "busy" was an accurate response. I am too busy to have anything compete with my own life and death. Of course, I have continued to have interests beyond myself, I still seek to learn from reading and listening to others, and I maintain an interest in solving the massive problems facing society. (I regret I won't be around another fifty years to see how we work them out.) Nonetheless, my principal preoccupations are the matters concerning my own life.

My psychological and emotional being needs to be expressed and recorded. I need to write more and in greater depth, not only because it helps me evolve and grow, but also in order to record this aspect of the journey. Big things are stirring deep within me. I am exceedingly "busy" with them.

Through this period, my prayer life has been like an arid desert. I just don't feel as if I am getting through, and I daresay God must be having the same problem with me. I have tried to pray, "Come on, God, let's get on with it," but there has been no comfort in such a prayer. So I changed to a less directive character: "God, be about it at your own speed, but I'm ready." I know that God is not a push-button God—one who responds to my will—but no matter how I said it, I knew I was seeking the execution of *my* schedule. I was still telling God what to do and expecting a response. It's difficult for me to relinquish being in charge, even in prayer. No wonder my prayer life has been dry. I have been asking God to function in my image.

Several mornings ago, I woke in a state of excitement, with a feeling of discovery and a heightened sense of peace and well-being. And in my mind were two phrases that seemed to sum it all up—*secure in the knowledge* and *trust and patience*. It all became so clear and obvious. I don't have to try to push God (as if I could) into some sort of timetable that will relieve my agonizing limbo; instead, I can await the unfolding of events and circumstances within God's dependable system called "life." I can be secure in the knowledge that:

- I am part of God's creation and system;
- The system is loving and good, possessing the nature of its Creator;
- God is in charge;
- All is well because God is Love;
- Jesus is proof of this; in His life, death, and resurrection, I need no other.

So I am secure in the knowledge of this and now must pray for trust and patience.

Nonetheless, I must observe that, except for Martha and Margo, I feel isolated and very much alone. I feel unable to talk with anyone but them about what matters in my life. Tom and Karen come close, but distance and infrequency of contact deny us.

Almost no one inquires about how Martha is doing in her own life.

> I haven't felt isolated until recently, but if I become too explicit about what's going on, people either get glassy-eyed or withdraw. When they ask how Chuck is, I'm learning that a simple answer of "OK"

satisfies most people. There are some friends to whom I can say that
he isn't doing as well as he was. Others can't understand how he can
be as ill as he is when he's out among people. We go to church, we
entertain (though much less), we show up at parties. Chuck laughs
and enjoys being with others, and he's interested in what's going on
in the world. He is stimulated by other people and camouflages his
discomforts. Participating in life is very important to Chuck, and
because of the pain pump, he's able to do it. If it weren't for that, he'd
have been eaten up by pain long since.

My hope is that he'll be able to enjoy life clear to the end, and
when he can no longer do that, he'll move quickly to the next dimension.

OCTOBER 14, 1993

I had lunch today with Bud Fisher, our attorney and long-time
friend. As we parted, there occurred one of those rare, precious
moments. I was about to get out of the car when he reached
over to hold me back and said, "Chuck, I love you."

Too often we don't quite get around to saying what is in our
hearts to say, and sometimes time runs out.

OCTOBER 15, 1993

A physician friend of mine who knows my attitude about healing asked me to visit one of his patients who, the doctor said,
wanted to consider the concept of healing as differentiated
from curing. Little did I know that the patient and his wife were
fundamentalists and Biblical literalists. The patient was one
week postop from a radical prostatectomy. It turned out to be
a meeting of questionable value to them and of considerable
uneasiness for me. This was clearly not the time to offer an attitude or belief that was potentially threatening to their rigidly
held convictions.

And then, out of the blue came the revelation that the wife
had once had cancer of the uterus that "God cured." Thirty
years ago, she was diagnosed with uterine cancer, but when a
hysterectomy was performed, no cancer was found. "We prayed
for God to cure my cancer and He did. There was no need for
surgery." Now they prayed for the patient's cancer to be cured—
but it wasn't. One can only imagine the intensity of their feelings.

As I left the room, I was convinced we'd been discussing the wrong subject. We should have been talking about his cancer and where he is now, not what I've dealt with for the past seven years. It was a learning experience for me.

OCTOBER 16, 1993

So what are the effects of the morphine? It manages pain, of course, and I am completely confident in its ability to do that, but because pain continues to break through the morphine as the tumors grow and the pain increases, frequent upward adjustments of the pump are required to successfully keep on top of the pain. Six months ago, I was taking 6 mg per twenty-four hours; today it's 30 mg, and at this rate six months from now, we'll be looking at a dosage of 150 mg. I can't help wondering about the impact of this wonderful, but powerful, narcotic. How much can I take in the name of pain management before significant side effects overwhelm me?

While the current dosage allows me to lead a more or less normal life, it appears it's beginning to exact a price. It could be that morphine is the scapegoat for physical and emotional changes. It's been interesting to note how quickly Bill points to morphine as the explanation of a change and how frequently Arthur expresses reservations about such conclusions. But there do seem to be personality changes that cause me to be guarded with Martha and others. Martha and I are increasingly having to deal with stress in our relationship, words with sharp edges which precipitate responses that I perceive to be attacks. And when I'm with others, I say things that are perceived far differently from what I intended. I find myself needing to hold back from commenting, at least until I consider what I am about to say or do.

Is this walking on eggs? I hope not. Martha and I have never done that. Perhaps, though, I need to be a bit more deliberate and responsible for my words and mannerisms, making room for whatever impact morphine may be having on my personality. There have been too many instances recently when my antennae picked up vibes that were uncomfortable.

Talking is the best way for Chuck and me to deal with problems, and we both pray a lot for guidance, courage, strength, and patience. I have felt sometimes as if I were praying a broken record, as if my prayers were always asking for the same things. Maybe, having asked several times, I don't need to do it again, but I find that God does hear, and when I'm listening and receptive, His answers come in many different ways.

As I'm walking my two miles in the morning, many times I'll gain an insight or I'll feel as if a weight is being lifted from me. Other times, in talking with Margo or in reading, I'll hear or read something in a new light. God does work in mysterious ways, as Mother always said. I can't say I hear the Holy Spirit speaking to me, but when I receive an insight or feel strength or a sense of peace being given to me, that is surely the Holy Spirit at work.

To combat our sharpness with one another and head off disagreements, Chuck and I decided we'd have a little signal to use when either one of us feels attacked by the other. Our signal is to pull on our right ears, which will permit the attacker to stop and think about what we're saying or doing. This morning, for instance, Chuck was hurting quite badly, and I wanted him to go sit in his chair until it was time to leave for church. I was really urging him to do that; when I turned around to look at him, he was pulling his ear. I realized I was bugging him, and I backed off. This signal is worth a try. These are precious days, as well as stressful ones, and since they are intricately woven together, we must deal with the whole.

Chuck and I have learned so much on this journey. We can see how easy it would be to become estranged, and that we don't want. There is no estrangement as we talk and talk and talk.

OCTOBER 19, 1993

This has been a very humbling day, a day that has me completely speechless. I don't know when I've been more at a loss for words, while at the same time, oh, so grateful.

Chuck read to me his feelings about his dependency on me and about the support and security he gets from me as I refresh his memory and walk beside him in many ways. Here are his words:

Throughout the many years of adulthood, I have never doubted my self-esteem and confidence, nor have I considered myself dependent on anyone. In our fifty years of marriage I have never felt dependent on Martha; if anything, I felt her dependence on me.

All of that has passed, and I feel dependent on her in so many ways. Increasingly Martha is my memory and my mirror, and more than that, she is my support and my security—physically, emotionally, and socially. It never occurred to me that this would come about, and I confess that it gives me a feeling of vulnerability to set it down this way.

We have often commented about the depth of our love for one another and about the closeness of our relationship, and we have said that even in the presence of our mutual sadness and occasional conflict, we have never felt closer or more in love. These fifty years have been a magnificent journey, diminished not one whit by the events of the last seven years.

I have said she is my memory. She gently and sensitively fills in to remind me of events, conversations, and experiences that frequently escape my mind, and she does it so effectively, I never feel any embarrassment or loss of self-esteem. And she is my mirror. I need to be in possession of all the facts, to be aware of the is-ness of things. So much of the world seems dedicated to withholding the truth from the patient. They tell me how well I look when I don't feel as if I do. Even physicians try to put a positive spin on their comments, requiring us to question them more forcefully in order to become as well informed as we'd like to be. So Martha is my mirror—openly and honestly telling me how I look and how she perceives me—even when, on occasion, she wonders if being so honest might be disturbing to me. I need to know, and I trust her to tell me truthfully.

She is there for support when I lose my equilibrium and start to fall. She is there to help me negotiate steps. She is there in a host of ways, not the least of which is simply being there. She supports me emotionally as, I daresay, I support her. She does it even amid her own stress and emotional turmoil. She supports me socially by reassuring me that my conduct has not been excessive and by heading me off when I appear to be on the road to self-destruction. These are but a few of the ways she supports me, but they are at the heart of my growing dependence on her in new and different ways. The glorious part of all this is that I'm not threatened, and I welcome this new relationship. As it blossoms and blooms, our love, respect, and admiration for each other are prospering.

It is different to have Chuck depend on me in areas where he has always been so sharp and quick. I don't like his loss of acuity, but cancer and morphine do take their toll.

Chuck gave me a wonderful gift today. Thank heaven I am able to give him some security, along with all my love.

OCTOBER 21, 1993

No one has been able to answer this question for me: Is unfelt pain debilitating? Margo says, "Your body knows you are in pain, but your mind doesn't."
I wonder.

OCTOBER 23, 1993

People seem unwilling to accept my morphine-induced loss of mental acuity and memory. Invariably they try to reassure me by attributing it to the aging process and tell me they too have memory problems. They tell me they note no loss of mental agility on my part.

Well, that's nice, but unbelievable to me. I know full well what's going on in my head—principally three things:

• simply forgetting (entire conversations, the extent or intensity of pain, people's names);
• an inability to solve relatively simple mental problems (in what year was a seventy-nine-year-old person born? what relative is someone's brother-in-law's wife?); and
• going blank in the middle of a conversation, simply because I've lost track of where I was or where I was going.

This loss is frustrating and embarrassing, but it's just one of those things I have to accept and live with. I wonder what it will be like, though, in the weeks or months to come, as my dosage goes up. Of this I'm sure, though: If it comes down to pain or loss of mental acuity, I'll take the loss of acuity.

OCTOBER 26, 1993

Another concession, this one enormous. We made it while we were walking. I dropped it on Martha like a bomb: "Let's not plan to go to Washington at Christmas." To my delight, Martha had been thinking the same thing.

There are two scenarios that could unfold. The first sees us planning to fly to Washington, hoping I have the strength and vitality to do it. The second admits the probability that my strength will continue to dwindle and that I'll be unable to go or, at best, will pay a great price for having attempted it. The first means putting off a final decision until just before Christmas, with great pressure building on me to go. The second takes all the pressure off and leaves the remote possibility of a last-minute change of plan and a Christmas-morning flight to D.C.

We've wondered for the past couple of years if that year's Christmas would be my last, and here we are, wondering again. But this year it seems a near certainty. So it is a great blow to plan not to go and will bring great disappointment to the kids, but now that we have thought it through, it seems intelligent, and it feels right, too.

OCTOBER 27, 1993

Martha and I recently visited a friend in the health-care center. Poor guy, he had given up on participating in life. Noting that there was no TV in his room nor any of the personal items that would create an ambiance of warmth and comfort, I said, "Charlie, how are you going to watch OSU football?"

He replied, "I don't give a damn about OSU football."

When we left, I realized that his attitude had dragged down not only his wife and daughter, but Martha and me as well. His wife later mentioned to us that she is worried because he has given up. I don't wonder at her concern.

His wife says he doesn't like to be questioned about how he feels or what the doctors have said, so she placates him by not asking him anything. It's sad. There doesn't seem to be any real communication between them, and it makes me wonder if it has always been that way. What a difference from Chuck!

Chuck is such a positive person, even when the reality of his disease surrounds him. He has always thought of the other person; he wants others to feel he has given something of himself to them, not handed them a burden. My Chuck loves life, his family, and his friends, and he wants them to know it. Knowing Chuck, I'm sure he will be that way until the end. What an inspiration he is!

OCTOBER 31, 1993

Saying a final goodbye is a new experience. As I have contemplated final moments with relatives and friends, I have concluded that I will need to express myself in a way totally personal and appropriate to the person.

I remember vividly the final goodbye exchanged between two brothers in our presence and that of a dozen or more others. Just observing it was painful to watch, and it was recorded indelibly in my memory. The cancer-ridden brother was speechless as his older brother strode across the room to embrace him, uttering only, "Goodbye, bro." He then turned and departed. Remembering, I concluded long ago that, painful as it might be, I would express myself meaningfully and probably, in most cases, would initiate the exchange.

My fear about this is not the emotion of the moment but the concern that I will choose a moment that, in fact, is not the final goodbye—that I will survive to see again the person to whom I've made my final farewells—sort of like an expectant mother returning home from the hospital after false labor, with no baby to show for it. It's bound to happen from time to time, and I guess there's no alternative but to accept the fact.

My first two final farewells occurred last week. My sister, Ruth, and her husband, Ray, came from Florida for their annual visit, and we knew it was improbable we would see one another again. This farewell was much easier than I had anticipated. I was able to say what I wanted to say, to tell her I love her, and to say goodbye. I don't even have an impression of how she felt; she camouflaged her feelings totally, but did manage to say, "I love you. You know that." Entirely in character, I thought.

Chuck carried off this event with such feeling, and he did it in a public restaurant as we were having breakfast. I was the only one with dry eyes, and that surprised me. I felt as if I were wrapped in a protective coating. I had steeled myself for this occasion, and I just wanted to get it over with. I hurt for Chuck and I hurt for Ruth, but I was powerless to say much. In fact, as we were driving back to church, Chuck talked to me about his feelings. After a while, he said my silence was deafening, to which I replied I didn't know what to say, and I really didn't.

In church I found it terribly hard to keep my mind on the service, and my praying was not good. My mind was so full of dealing with the fact that Chuck was actually saying goodbyes, and I knew this was just the beginning. How was I going to react? Would I always feel as if I were wrapped in plastic or in steel armor in order to protect myself? I know I'm protecting myself because it hurts so much. I don't like anything that makes Chuck's death seem more imminent. I'm afraid to toss off the coating because then I'll be more vulnerable to hurt.

As I walked this morning, I told God that all I could do was turn myself over to Him and to trust. I have trusted all along, but I realize I've kept a piece of myself shielded. He knows it, and now I know it.

The second farewell caught my friend Gil by surprise. He was to leave the next morning for his winter condo in Florida, not to return again until next May. Again I had thought through what I wanted to say, which I expressed as we embraced. His response came the next day in a beautiful, warm letter that fed my soul.

These two experiences have been exhilarating for me, and I have gained confidence that those to follow will be equally enriching. Thank God, I can talk and express myself in this way. To remain silent when a final farewell is at hand must leave an emptiness in the soul.

NOVEMBER 18, 1993

Our excitement is enormous as we contemplate our fiftieth anniversary, now only three days away. Having already celebrated it with the family two years ago, because Stan doubted I would be here for the real thing, gives the approaching day a special meaning.

NOVEMBER 23, 1993

The apartment is awash in blessed silence. They have all gone home. The entire family was here for the special day. They put on an event never to be forgotten. A flowering crab apple tree was planted in our courtyard, symbolic of the roots we have given them. We also received a wren house, whose occupants will symbolize the wings we also gave them. The celebration included a five-course catered gourmet dinner, a wedding cake, and numerous gifts in a light vein.

> The entire weekend we were blessed with flowers, cards, and calls from friends, beginning with Margo, who brought a special card and French pastries and a bottle of champagne for our Friday morning breakfast.

Martha caught immediately the symbolism of my gift to her.

> Chuck surprised me with an eight-sided gold pendant holding two pieces of glass that encased a beautiful single piece of gold shaped into a serpentine thread—a reminder of Patrice's comment that there is a golden thread running between us, from heart to heart, that will never be broken. This pendant Chuck had designed especially.
>
> When I opened it, I gave a gasp and the tears flowed. Words are not capable of telling my joy, my happiness, and my deep feelings

when my eyes fell on this special piece of jewelry, this symbol of love. What a privilege to be married for fifty years and what a privilege to be married to Chuck for those years! Our journey has been one of love, spiritual growth, much other growth, and doing things together. We really are the Velcro Kids!

The event wasn't without humor when Max (age six), observing me urinating in the men's room, noticed my prosthesis-engorged penis and commented to me twice (as if I had missed it the first time), "Chuck, you have a BIG penis," and then, as if that weren't enough, he went back to the dining room and announced the same amazing fact to everyone still at the table. What a bird!

The next day, we gathered at church, all sitting together in the front pew. The rector introduced each of us, and the congregation applauded and joined in the joyful moment. There was even a single red rose placed on the baptismal font in our honor by Michael and Barbara Jupin. A single red rose had been on the altar of the church where we were married, so it was very meaningful.

After church, I had the great joy of presenting each of the family with an item I had selected from my possessions. I told them that usually when people go on a trip, they bring a gift on their return, but in due course, I'd be taking a trip from which I wouldn't return, and thus I felt it appropriate to give them their presents now, before my departure.

For me, it was a precious moment.

DECEMBER 8, 1993

The pump is now set at 50 mg per twenty-four hours. Ah, morphine! What a wonderful drug! Dr. H. says that if he were to take the drug at the dosage I'm receiving, he'd stop breathing, but I tolerate the gradual increase in my dosage well. There seems to be no maximum limit that can be predicted. It differs with each patient. Arthur relies heavily on my judgment for the dosage, obviously under his watchful eye. Wouldn't it be great, I said to him, if we could come to some kind of acceptance of my probable date of death and increase the dosage gradually in order to come out even—zonking out about the time I die? Dr. H. gave that idea little room. He, like Bill, is unwilling to predict longevity.

A new development is a swelling near the scar of the incision made to install the catheter in my spine. A tumor? Arthur didn't

think so. A leak in the catheter? He's wondering about that. He
wants to watch it for a while and see what develops. It's strange
how little it concerns me. I expect that episodes, events, and situations are going to occur unannounced, unpredicted, acute,
and troublesome.

These episodes draw on my reserve of acceptance again and
again, tolerating first this and then that, but at the same time
they keep in focus the wonder and joy of this amazing journey.

DECEMBER 15, 1993

It's only ten days until Christmas, and there never seems to be
enough time. It's very important to me to send Christmas bread to
Tom and Karen and their families; it's a tradition from my parents'
family which we have carried on. Mother made the bread and the
Santa cookies and the Santa's boot cookies until she could no longer
do it. Then I took over.

All of us were to meet at Tom and Carol's, but we have opted to
remain at home this year. I felt I had to send the bread, and that I did.
I've had to forego the cookies, however, because I have had an attack
of vertigo and have been told to slow down. That's hard, but if Chuck
can make concessions, so can I.

DECEMBER 27, 1993

A few weeks ago, when Martha asked what I wanted for Christmas, I answered, "How about consumables?" It occurred to me
that selecting gifts for a fellow living on borrowed time presents
something of a problem. Well, it turned out to be a wonderful
Christmas from the point of view of gifts received. Look at
what I got:

• Six filets mignons;
• A pound of lox and two lobster tails;
• A fifty-dollar gift certificate to be redeemed at the Kroger fish
  department;
• A case of fine wine from Italy and a bottle of New York State
  red wine; and
• A bowl with six hyacinth bulbs which we can watch bloom
  during the winter.

I loved it!

JANUARY 1, 1994

For many years, I've struggled with the concept of the Holy Spirit. Only since I became an Episcopalian has it been of great importance, however. In our previous church little reference was made to this aspect of the Trinity. But in the Episcopal liturgy, one gets confronted with the Holy Spirit again and again, and I couldn't seem to dodge the issue.

I wakened this morning in an excited state, and the word on my lips was "presence." It all fell into place. The Holy Spirit is the presence of God and Jesus Christ in my life. It seemed clear—not profound, but clear.

JANUARY 23, 1994

It has been said that cancer patients see their friends withdraw. While we haven't had much of that yet, we have wondered if it might happen. Perhaps we have arrived at that place. At least we can imagine the circumstances that might cause our friends to withdraw.

As my fatigue and weakness have increased, I've been unable to continue at my once-typical pace. So first we began to invite friends for bridge at midafternoon, followed by dinner and our guests' early departure. My morphine was increased, my short-term memory was impaired, and we conceded bridge.

Then we invited friends for dinner at 5:00, and by 8:30 they left. We met folks for breakfast—a much better time of day for me—or occasionally for brunch or lunch. They reciprocated generously, and we expressed our gratitude that they were willing to turn around their social schedules for us. We began to feel uncomfortable when others entertained us, however, particularly when other guests were invited and were being inconvenienced on our behalf.

A few days ago, we attended a dinner party scheduled for an early hour to enable our early departure. It hadn't been a good day for me, and my participation did little to make it a lively party. Our leaving at 8:00 p.m. surely broke the atmosphere so important to any hostess.

Yesterday we declined a dinner invitation because it was scheduled for 6:30. It doesn't take a lot of imagination to see that it soon will be easier for others not to include us, nor should they. To build their schedules around us is asking more than they should undertake. We understand, but it hurts. And it hurts me to see us participate in less and less, to see Martha's life become increasingly drab, with a shrinking agenda of things to look forward to. Do the concessions ever stop?

JANUARY 26, 1994

We knew the day would come when we were told we were in the final phase, the day when everything says the end is coming. That day was yesterday. First we viewed with Patrice the raw tape of a television program for which we had been interviewed in early November. We're not sure when we last viewed the tape, but we were shocked at the change in my appearance and expression in the brief time since November.

Then we saw Bill, who confirmed all my feelings. He is so good at explaining why I feel as I do and what will probably occur as time passes. Stan had called the final phase "escape" and identified its feature as a PSA of greater than 60. Bill calls it a failure of hormonal treatment and places its onset at the time when the PSA turns around and resumes its upward climb. Bill points to forty weeks as the average survival time after failure. Stan gave an average of six months after escape.

No matter: my PSA is 59.3, and I am now fifty weeks post-failure. Bill predicts my deterioration will accelerate markedly, and although metastasis to a vital organ could precipitate an acute problem, he foresees general decline until the end. We talked briefly about my death and dying, and I told him I hoped he would help me die in peace. With profound gentleness, he agreed.

We came home numb; the process of dying is upon us. When we entered the apartment, I put my arms around Chuck, and as I felt his arms around me, I sobbed.

Later, as I walked, I truly opened myself up to God. I have to get myself out of the way in order to feel His strength within me. Now I'm on an even keel again.

Looking ahead is hard, and if I dwell on it, I'll miss the beauty of this day. It isn't necessary to look ahead more than one day at a time. It's been more than seven years since Chuck was diagnosed, and taking each day at a time, we've been able to enjoy every one.

FEBRUARY 15, 1994

What a birthday celebration—more than forty cards, four bouquets, numerous telephone calls, fruit, cookies, other goodies from friends, but most of all, Tom and Karen here for a visit! Karen brought two live lobsters from Boston which, together with Tom's Christmas steaks, formed a surf-and-turf dinner. Both kids had come for Martha's seventieth birthday. We wondered if the joy of gathering the "original team" could be duplicated, and it was!

> To have the original eight feet under the dining table was a precious experience. Staying home was a sacrifice Carol and Doug made as their gift to Chuck.

Then came a visit to Dr. H. to refill the pump. During the last two fillings, more residual fluid remained in the pump than should have been there, considering the current dosage level. The computer said there should be 2 cc remaining; actually there were 8 cc. Did the pump shortchange me? Was there a kink in the catheter that was restricting the flow? Or could it have been a malfunction of the one-way valve, allowing spinal fluid to flow back into the tank?

> It has all been a big mystery and is of concern to us. Dr. H. said if the pump isn't working properly, he'll have to replace it. Also, the bump in Chuck's spine around the catheter has turned hard. I wonder if that's coincidental or part of the whole picture.
>
> Arthur now wants more lab work, so we have to wait for eleven days for the CT scan. The pain pump has been such a wonderful thing; I hope any problem can be easily rectified. I should be used to limbo now, as it seems we've been in that state since Chuck's remission ended.

FEBRUARY 16, 1994

Sitting in my living-room chair, dressed in my pajamas and robe, sipping a glass of wine, speaking by phone to my long-time friend, Doug Krieger, I bought Martha a new car. It had long been my stated purpose to do this as a final act for her, postponing the day she would have to make this decision alone.

We have yet to turn 19,000 miles on our present car—WOW! But what the heck! I did it anyway. I did it and I'm glad. So there!

FEBRUARY 21, 1994

What a wonderful time we had with our granddaughter, Nicole! At sixteen, she is a seasoned traveler, so she arrived by herself for an overnight with us.

We had a lovely day, and after Chuck went to bed, she and I stayed up to watch the Olympics for a short time. Then we turned off the TV and talked. I asked her how she felt about losing Chuck, a grandfather she dearly loves. She hesitated for a moment and then said she was surprised at how much better he looked than she had anticipated. Very quietly, she went on to say she knew that death was a part of life and that Chuck would have a rebirth into another life. She mentioned she knew she would feel Chuck's presence and influence in her life because she still feels my mother's presence and influence on her. She then talked about a dark death–that which occurs when someone is killed suddenly or before he has an opportunity to live a full life.

Our conversation then turned to God, and I asked her what her "handhold" was, mine being that I know God is always with me. Nicole said she didn't believe in God because she couldn't see or feel Him. We talked about spirituality, which also can't be seen or felt. We came to an understanding when she said there are times when she feels the answer to something mysteriously come to her or when she has had a moment of intense joy. We talked about her caring for others and about how her friends depend on her. She wanted to know why I thought God was with her; I answered that it was because I could see the loving and caring that is so much a part of her nature. She is searching, and that's good.

Margo said on the phone this evening how wonderful it is that our family have come to see us and to share this time with us. Not only have they all come together, but each one has had a special time with Chuck and me. We feel so blessed! Margo says she doesn't see this kind of support very often and is so pleased for us now.

FEBRUARY 23, 1994

For some time, Martha and I have been urging the administration of the Village to begin exploratory conversation with their counterparts at Riverside Hospice. Martha and I were delighted yesterday to find out that the two institutions have agreed to use us as guinea pigs and to provide us with all hospice services here in our apartment and, if required, in the health-care center or clinic.

FEBRUARY 28, 1994

Oh, m'gosh, it's surgery again! Hard to believe, but the catheter has extricated itself from my spine. "There's what we need to know," Dr. H. said, as he gazed into the screen of the fluoroscope. There was the catheter, all coiled up under my skin. How long has it been pumping morphine into the tissue outside the spine? Perhaps since last September, and surely since December, when we noticed a small lump under the skin.

It didn't take long for us to decide what to do. Continuing as we were would push excessive amounts of morphine through my system and produce little analgesia. That seemed an unattractive alternative, so we decided to replace the pump tomorrow.

MARCH 12, 1994

March came in like a lion as far as I was concerned. It began with me back at the James again—and how I looked forward to this operation after the gargantuan headaches, nausea, and vomiting of the last go-round!

We had been congratulating ourselves on our attitudes and on the fact that we hadn't been at each other the way we were prior to other surgeries. Boy, were we wrong! On February 28, we fell apart. I was very sensitive to Chuck's overpreciseness, and he was aware that the tone of my voice and my flashing eyes showed my patience was wearing thin. We didn't like the situation, but we couldn't seem to stop. The morning of surgery, we felt so bad and needed healing. Slowly but surely we began to talk, and by the time we left for the hospital, we were OK.

Melody came to the hospital with some blessed oil she placed on Chuck's forehead while she prayed with us. That was a special moment.

The surgery was scheduled to take two hours, so when I had heard nothing after three hours, I was fearful. I remembered the last time when complications lengthened the surgery. I was scared something like that had happened again, but it hadn't. The surgery had simply begun later than expected. Melody, Bud, and Ann stayed with me; Margo came over before surgery but then had to go back to work.

It was good to see Chuck. When I walked into his room, his bed was at a thirty-degree elevation, and he was feeling good. In fact, when his dinner came, it was a full meal—beef stroganoff, of all things. Dr. H. came in, looked at the meal, and told Chuck to take it easy. Good advice. I ate most of it. I was so pleased with how he felt, but I was leery, because this was how it had been the last time, too. I went home a happy gal, however.

The next morning Chuck called to say he'd vomited his dinner and now was struggling with nausea and vomiting again. He was a sick puppy. For the entire day, the doctors and nurses worked to eliminate the nausea. At one point he was wheeled to radiology to make sure the catheter was still in the right place. The trip almost did him in, so he was finally given a medication that knocked him out.

In addition to making him very sleepy, the medication caused him to act out his dreams. He had the busiest hands you can imagine. He dealt cards, picked up imaginary items, opened imaginary cupboard doors. When he was awake, he would slip off into dreams and talk about things out of context. He knew he was doing this, and it embarrassed him. It was hard to watch, especially when he asked me if I saw the men in the room or when he talked about events he thought were taking place.

One of the medications they gave me was Scopolamine, which gave me nearly every side effect the manufacturers warned about, not the least of which was hallucinations. I was really off the wall. I can't believe people rob banks to finance getting drugs like these.

Finally, four days after surgery, Chuck was released.

Before leaving the hospital, they increased the dosage on the pump from 2.1 to 3.0, and then to 4.0, which is adequate for pain control but leaves me drowsy. Some difference from the 75 mg per day I was getting before the surgery, when probably 95 percent of it was being systematically dissipated into the tissue surrounding my spine, with little impact on pain. Now my pain is largely gone, but stay tuned. There's never a dull moment.

MARCH 14, 1994

We are brittle and stressed and contentious. That last word is one I don't like and never thought I'd have to use to describe Chuck and me.

This evening, I misunderstood something he said about his medication, and I made matters worse by saying his memory hasn't been all that accurate. That made him very unhappy, and he said he wasn't feeble-minded. Of course he isn't, but the last few weeks have been hard on his acuity and memory. He had asked me for help concerning his medication but then had made out a chart to remind himself of the doses and times. I neglected to remind him, because I thought he was in charge of his medications again. I felt bad that I'd forgotten to remind him, so this time I overreacted the other way. It's no wonder we're getting into snits. I'm coming through too strongly, and Chuck's trying extra hard to show he's OK. When my words or actions make him feel less OK, that's not good.

Dear God, what am I doing or not doing? What am I missing? Is all this part of the separation process? I hope not, because we've never been like this, and it's perplexing to both of us.

Today was a heavy day in another way as well. The hospice requires a letter from the patient's physician saying he has about six months' life expectancy. It was very hard to see that in print.

MARCH 22, 1994

Yesterday was the initial visit from Riverside Hospice. They came three strong—my attending nurse, my social worker, and a nurse trainee. It was a good session. I was reassured immeasurably.

> Because it's difficult for me to know whom to call if Chuck has a different kind of pain or upset (should I call the urologist or the pain center or Dr. Cindi?), I'll call hospice. They will come see Chuck and call the correct doctor. Bill told us it will be a big help to him to talk with another professional, so that's reassuring. Professionals like the hospice nurses know better how to evaluate Chuck than does his anxious wife. I'm very pleased with this arrangement.

MARCH 23, 1994

Bill reported that my PSA is down! Still, it's 58.7. He and I agreed that the test is of little further value, so it will be discontinued as part of my periodic evaluation.

MARCH 25, 1994

When we saw Bill and Dr. H. recently, we explained that we were very confused when we received what appeared to be contradictory advice from them and that we felt the need for a "campaign director"—one person who is in charge but who talks with everyone else. We actually pled for such an arrangement.

The reason for this request was a most disquieting episode in which Bill, having prescribed Motrin for my extreme leg pain, had changed it to another medication, called Toradol.

Learning of this the first time, Arthur had been obviously distressed. "Did Bill know you're taking Trilisate?" he asked. I assured Dr. H. that Bill had it in his chart; as a matter of fact, moments before Bill's recommendation, I had reviewed all my medications with the resident.

Arthur's distress came from the fact that I was on the maximum recommended dose of Trilisate (under his direction) and that both Motrin (of which I had taken the maximum dose) and Toradol (for which Bill had recommended the maximum dosage) were from the same family of medications as Trilisate. Thus I had been taking and was being directed to take twice the recommended dosage and was a good candidate for "their eating a hole in your stomach with all the attendant risks of hemorrhage." Arthur's subsequent conversation with Bill brought the statement from Bill that he was unaware I was on Trilisate. Read that as "I didn't check the chart before I prescribed the Motrin or Toradol."

Now, I call that a close call, which never would have been caught had we not requested an appointment with Dr. H. while we were at the James seeing Bill. In any event, all this brought about better consultation between the two and a definition of responsibilities that puts Arthur in charge of my pain and Bill in charge of everything else.

APRIL 1, 1994

I've had two vivid dreams which are essentially the dreams I have when I can't seem to get a handle on things that are happening. In the first, we were purchasing a new car, and I simply couldn't fill out the papers correctly. In the second, I was sitting with Mother, Florence Worrell, and Chuck at our dining table, which was covered with my best damask tablecloth. I was constantly spilling something on the cloth—wine, tea, gravy—all real stain-makers. I spilled everything I picked up.

Margo agreed that my dreams signified my frustration about not being able to make things come out well organized, but she also asked me to write them down and think about them some more. She said there was another message in those dreams. I realized that both dreams pointed to my feelings of inadequacy. Wow, did that turn on a light bulb! I was feeling inadequate about caring by myself for

Chuck, to whom I have always turned for advice and help. It's interesting that the second dream was about Mother, Florence, and Chuck, for the three of them had always been my mentors.

APRIL 9, 1994

We've been advised that the stress we both feel is likely to erupt from time to time. Indeed, that has been occurring with increased frequency in recent weeks, producing deep regret in both our hearts—and adding even more stress.

It blossomed into a major disruption a week ago. Martha's church responsibilities became concentrated in a three- or four-day period which required our being apart several hours a day, more than either of us desired. During this period, I felt particularly miserable, which compounded my feelings of loneliness and abandonment. Martha, poor dear, was on overload, hardly able to handle what was already on her plate, let alone her feelings of guilt and of being "beaten on" by me.

We're pleased with the manner in which we worked it through, but we both felt more than a little fear that it had gone too far, that we were "off the tracks." I made some notes about what I learned from this painful and difficult time:

- I am failing and need both physical and psychological help.
- When help comes, I often perceive it to be at the sacrifice of my independence, integrity, and individual worth.
- We are both fragile.
- I want to support Martha's life beyond these four walls. She feels this support, but she also feels my need for her presence and touch, and it leaves her fragmented.
- We need to trust that which has brought us to this moment and will sustain us.

APRIL 15, 1994

As I signed our federal tax return, I commented that there is at least some satisfaction in knowing this is the last one.

APRIL 18, 1994

It is all very strange and so different from what I expected. From the beginning we've been told that loss of appetite was a sure sign of the final stage of this disease. To be sure, my appetite is not as robust as it has been, but I do eat most of what Martha puts in front of me, and she keeps the quantities reasonable to avoid overwhelming me. Food still tastes good, but my interest in it has waned. Food doesn't sound as good as formerly; the idea of food is not particularly appealing. Strange.

APRIL 23, 1994

The people from Riverside Hospice have been a great help in keeping me honest about my feelings, as they are so truthful about the changes going on in Chuck's body. Michelle, the primary nurse, has talked with all of Chuck's physicians, and they are pleased to work with her. It certainly helps us by giving us a "commanding officer" to coordinate all the doctors. Chuck has been startled and anxious lately; Michelle talked with the physicians about that, and they put him on Valium. What a difference that makes! Also his bone pain just wasn't being relieved effectively, so she suggested another medication to Arthur, who agreed for Chuck to try it. It has worked wonders. It's such a relief to have someone orchestrating all these changes.

As we walked today, Martha asked about hope. Do we have hope? we asked ourselves. Of course we do. My hope is for the possible. I hope for:

- the continuing love and support of my family and friends, even in moments when I may become unlovable;
- a growing and enriching relationship with Martha and the children, tenderly and gently expressed;
- acceptance of whatever happens;
- a comfortable, relatively pain-free death;
- time and the ability to say thank-you and goodbye to friends and family;
- living these days in a way that inspires others;
- the ability to support my family in their hurt;
- the continuing enrichment of my spiritual life;
- mental acuity and alertness that will support my knowledge and growth;
- the ability for Martha and me to continue our objective of looking beyond ourselves; and
- reconciliation and restoration to wholeness—healing.

APRIL 18, 1994

All of my friends are conscious of what's going on and are eager to help in any way they can. I've finally had to admit to myself I need to make some changes. I don't want to neglect my responsibilities to the organizations I belong to, but my priority is to take care of Chuck. How do I do that and still stay in touch with the outside world?

Everyone is very understanding. I am so fortunate to have a vice president of the Women of St. Mark's who has asked me to meet with her and to talk with her about what she needs to do to step into my president's role when Chuck needs me at home more constantly. She and I are going to talk with Michael so that she is comfortable keeping him in touch with what's going on. She is a most capable young woman, and I have no hesitation about turning things over to her.

APRIL 26, 1994

We have another new phrase in our lives. Michelle came today, and in telling us about the status of some of her other patients, she used the phrase "in decline." Decline, she said, is the final, obvious downhill slide to the end. I asked her if I was in decline, and she said she had observed a decline in the month she's been with us, but she hastened to add that the rate of decline varies from patient to patient. She also mentioned that metastatic prostate cancer is often slower than others.

APRIL 29, 1994

Michelle calls it "tumor fever"—a condition that produces massive, soaking sweats, day or night, sometimes actually preceded by a fever. This morning, Martha commented on how warm I was—confirmed by a temperature reading of 101.6°. By the time we reached Michelle, I had broken into quite a sweat, and my temperature was normal.

MAY 14, 1994

This is the weekend Brian is graduating from William and Mary, and needless to say, we had hoped to be there. We hadn't counted on it, though. It's great Chuck is alive and able to experience the excitement vicariously. Our hearts are full of gratitude for such a wonderful grandson. We have so enjoyed watching him grow and develop. It really doesn't seem as if it's been twenty-one years, but it has, and it's been a privilege.

Another bump has appeared in Chuck's back at the same place

where the catheter worked itself out before. It's not as spongy, but this is the way it started before, and we are anxious, even a little paranoid, about its coming out again.

MAY 16, 1994

Another piece of the puzzle fell into place today. When Chuck was telling Michelle about his drowsiness, she explained that some of it was fatigue from the cancer itself, not from the Elavil he's been taking. She mentioned the same thing last week, but he didn't grasp the nuance. As Chuck described how the drowsiness comes and goes, she was very helpful in assuring him that this was the pattern of the disease. Strange as it seems, it made him feel better to let go of the idea that it was the medication and accept that it was part of the cancer.

He has felt so poopy the last three days, yet there were times he seemed better. Going into the parish hall after church is good for him, as is going to breakfast, but after about an hour or so, he's had it. Getting into his lounge chair restores him, and in all cases he perks up at midafternoon until about 7:00 p.m.

JUNE 12, 1994

Dr. B. told Chuck he looked better than Bill had expected. That pleased us, especially because this wasn't one of Chuck's better days. The small mass in his back seemed to have gone down, although the pain was still there. Bill wasn't concerned about it, since it had diminished in size.

Chuck asked him where his tumors were now, and Bill said they were in the pelvis, lymph nodes, and aorta. He said he wouldn't be surprised if there were also some in his lungs. This was the first time we knew the cancer was in his soft tissues as well as his bones. It was a jolt! Chuck was surprised to hear about the soft-tissue involvement, but he was encouraged to know the reason he was feeling so lousy. I've had to struggle with this information for a couple of days. I hadn't considered the possibility the cancer would invade the soft tissues.

I'm sad and I'm hurting! I have such mixed emotions. I don't want to lose Chuck, but I don't want him to suffer or to miss any quality of life. The new information doesn't change his prognosis, but I feel as though the other shoe will drop soon.

I'm so angry about this cancer! I really thought I had dealt with that feeling eight years ago and was surprised when it reappeared this evening. I was lying in bed watching the news while Chuck slept, when suddenly I was angry we couldn't share the news together. I know it's normal to feel angry, and I'm glad I recognize it rather than drive it underground by denying it.

JUNE 22, 1994

Chuck has always had shy bowels, but with the intake of narcotics, his bowels refuse to respond without a great deal of encouragement. He has been on Dulcolax for two years, and it has helped immensely, but there have been times when diarrhea has accompanied flatulence in the middle of the night. The other night he had an accident and soiled himself, the pajamas, and the bed. He felt so humiliated, in spite of the fact that I understood and was happy to help him get cleaned up. He is such a proud, independent person, and to have this happen deprives him of his dignity.

Michelle told us about a patient who died over the weekend. He had been as impatient as Chuck is about the yo-yo effect of this disease. He died unexpectedly on Sunday night. She mentioned that his cancer was not as far advanced as Chuck's appears to be.

It's strange, but having her tell us that brought me comfort. I hope Chuck can go that way, too. I don't want him to die, but I don't want him to linger and put up with a lot of humiliation because he becomes dependent. Yet I know it's not up to me to say what path Chuck will take. Time will tell.

JULY 2, 1994

We are so pleased with the people and the philosophy of the hospice organization. Our only concern has been about who will be in charge if Chuck should have to go to the health-care center here at the Village. We all agree he'll not go there unless he needs more care than I can give or I'm exhausted being the caregiver.

I have balked at the idea of the health-care center because I want him here. After some talking and tears, I finally understand that the only reason Chuck has thrown it into the mix is he isn't sure how much care he'll need and is so concerned I'll wear myself out. He's always said he'd prefer to die at home, but he wants me to keep my options open, since we have no idea what's ahead. We talked about private duty nurses and agreed a night nurse might be advisable for a short time at the end.

I don't want Chuck worrying about me. I want him to have peace. He can have no peace if I'm exhausted or fighting those who are trying to help me. I feel more secure in considering all the options. This part of the journey is hard enough without my attitude being one of resistance.

JUNE 23, 1995

I try to let Chuck be as independent as he can be, but it's a balancing act, as it's sometimes impossible for me to know how he's feeling. We do pretty well, but there are times when I misread him.

This week I've had several outside commitments. I try to guard my activities, but occasionally they bunch up. Chuck is so good about this when it happens, yet I know it's hard on him to have me gone or even preoccupied about an outside activity. Nonetheless, he doesn't want me to be cut off from the world, and he encourages me to stay involved as best I can.

Knowing how insecure Chuck and I are when we're apart, Tom gave me a cellular phone for Mother's Day. What a wonderful thing it is! Chuck can contact me when I'm on my walk or if I happen to go out for lunch or shopping. It's almost like a tether and is a great security blanket for both of us.

JUNE 20, 1994

What a Father's Day! Martha and I attended early services at church and arrived home about 9:15. I was in the bedroom, about to change my clothes, when the doorbell rang. I opened it, and there stood Tom! He had taken a very early flight from D.C. to get here. I was overwhelmed. We took him to the airport to catch a midafternoon flight back to Washington for his Father's Day with his kids.

We are so blessed by our kids. They just keep on caring and loving and acting on it.

JULY 2, 1994

I had gone to the bathroom, leaving Martha and Michelle conversing in the den. "I know Chuck is concerned about lingering through a protracted decline," I heard Michelle say. "But, Martha, I don't think he needs to worry about that." When Martha asked why, Michelle remarked on the progression she had observed recently.

Michelle thus confirmed my feeling that everything is becoming more—more pain, persisting longer; more weakness, now a constant companion; more fatigue, resulting in more sleep and more naps; more lack of interest in food—more of everything, it seems, almost on a daily basis.

JULY 4, 1994

I find it harder and harder to stay awake in my chair after dinner. Often Martha has to waken me to start me to bed, and once in bed, I am asleep literally in seconds.

Last evening Martha had difficulty arousing me. Once she succeeded, I rose on legs that had been unusually weak all day. On my way to bed, the collapse was instantaneous. Martha responded to my call immediately, held me up to pee, and finally settled me in bed. During the night, I used my cane to assist me to and from the bathroom. There is now so little strength in my legs, I just don't trust them.

JULY 6, 1994

The only time we can have with our friends besides going to church is at breakfasts, and those breakfasts mean a great deal to both of us. Yesterday and today, Chuck was so weak, and even though pillows surrounded him, the seats in the restaurant started up his back pain. It was hard for him and hard for me to watch. Bless his heart, he keeps on enjoying the company, but it's getting increasingly difficult. We'll eat out as long as we can. When it gets too tough, perhaps we can have friends here. We'll just have to wait and see what the future brings.

There is nothing more I want to do than to protect Chuck's dignity. As time goes on, he'll lose more and more of his independence, but I pray, no matter what, I can help him preserve his dignity.

JULY 7, 1994

In humor, I've previously referred to the portion of my body from waist to knees as my disaster area. So many things have been done to me there. Following each procedure, my ability to urinate has been temporarily impaired, necessitating the use of a straight catheter. As time has passed, it has required conscious effort to bear down and empty my bladder.

There are times when it takes him forty-five minutes to void his urine, but the average is usually about thirty minutes. The difficult thing for him is that his weak legs make it difficult for him to stand to urinate. Sleepiness and weakness aren't helpful. I sit on the edge of the tub and talk with him and urge him to bear down so he can go, but he falls asleep before he can accomplish anything. There I am, patting his hands, calling to him to wake up and bear down. I feel like a cheerleader. After he's tried sitting down, he'll stand with my arms around him and my feet braced for balance, in case his knees buckle.

There's humor in everything, and this is no exception. As I keep urging him to bear down, he'll sometimes make a noise as though he's doing so, but I know he's not, so I say, "No fair, you'll have to try again." Other times when he's standing up, he'll want to put his head on the cupboards behind the toilet so he can sleep, and I won't let him do it. It really is a riot, and I'm sure it would make a hilarious home movie. Finally, go or no go, it's time to get him back to bed. He'll try again later.

Both Bill and Michelle have said the time will come when I will have to have a Foley catheter permanently. It's difficult to conceal the presence of a Foley, since the urine is emptied into a bag, and it's even more difficult to deal with the catheter and hoses at night. The threat of that keeps me trying desperately to pee under my own power. I've had far too much exposure to a Foley to accept it as a permanent fixture. We may come to it, however, for my own safety. Michelle has suggested a portable potty to be set beside my bed. Maybe down the road, but for now I object to turning our bedroom into a bathroom. What a mess! It tries my patience, to say the least.

> The medication has nearly stopped his ability to move his bowels. Because there's no dynamite for such occasions, he takes a stool softener, mineral oil, and a very strong laxative. After two to three days, it works. However, there is the potential for an accident when he's sleeping, so we're trying to work out a formula that will give him results without accidents.

JULY 18, 1994

We recently picked up Karen at the airport for her fifth visit since the first of the year. As we drove home, I noted my driving was sloppy; I was literally all over the road. Having for years promised Martha I would stop driving the minute it was suggested I should, I wondered if the time might be approaching.

The next morning as we walked, Martha told me a few things about her evening conversation with Karen, and then after an interminable silence she brought up the subject of my driving. As she talked, I came to some realizations. I know my legs have become so weak that I question if I can hit the brake quickly enough in an emergency, because I know a fraction of a second's delay translates into many yards on the road. I reached into my pocket and put my keys in Martha's hand. The moment of truth had arrived for me, and I redeemed my promise.

In a way I feel proud of myself, but it does represent another concession, this one of great magnitude. One's wheels are a symbol of mobility and independence. To be without them leaves me with an empty feeling and one of dependence on Martha and others simply to get from point A to point B. Getting into the car, a simple act, now underscores the distance I have come on this trip with cancer.

JULY 19, 1994

Yesterday I gave up driving. Today I fell trying to get out of the bathtub. I may have cracked a rib. There is surely a bruise, but it's getting better.

> Chuck's falling was a jolt for both of us, because it caused me to realize there are things I can't do for him as his caregiver. I can't get him out of the tub or lift him at all when he can't help me. I have to have assistance available.
>
> Bless Riverside Hospice and First Community Village, as they both swung into action to help out. The hospice arranged for a tub chair and a handgrip on the side of the tub, and the Village installed a handheld shower head. This way, Chuck can sit on the chair in the tub and wash and rinse himself with the shower head. It's the best of all worlds, as he can feel independent and not worry about getting in or out of the tub.
>
> The concession that comes with all this new equipment is that we can no longer take our buddy baths. We've taken them frequently our entire married life, but since Chuck's retirement, it's been every day. Now we've had to concede that, too.

These changes caused Michelle to say, "Well, Chuck and Martha, we are now experiencing the progression of decline we've been anticipating, marking the beginning of the final phase."

To this I said, "I'm ready."

She replied, "I know you are."

> My heart is so sad but filled with such gratitude for all the people who are helping us though this difficult time.

JULY 31, 1994

One day last week, Colby asked his mother if she would pay for him to fly out here and spend the day with us. Her instantaneous, affirmative reply set in motion his arrival this morning. The next eight hours were absolutely superb—with talking and loving as three people perhaps have never done before. Colby boned chicken for Martha, helped us select a new cordless phone, and programmed the memory numbers. He shared the thoughts and feelings of a college sophomore and made kind and loving comments about us, his grandparents, that warmed our hearts.

Suddenly, it was all over and we dumped him off at the airport for his return to Boston. His final act was to open the front passenger door beside me and insert his upper body into the car. Then together we had a final goodbye and embrace. It was so tender, endearing, and filled with emotion. I don't know what we whispered in each other's ears, but tender words were spoken, and then he was gone.

His brother Brian had been here in June, and we had had a similar experience. How wonderful to have such young men as part of our family!

AUGUST 2, 1994

Michelle was here this morning, and I told her Chuck had really gone down since she was here a week ago, and when she saw him she agreed there had been a lot of change.

Michelle was so helpful, as always, reminding us we'd be seeing changes daily. Therefore, it's OK to be anxious for each other. I worry about Chuck, and he worries about me. We have always lived each day to the fullest, but Michelle's emphasis was to live for each day and what it brings and not to worry about what tomorrow has in store. Be prepared, she said, and take each day as it comes.

Tonight it was so difficult for Chuck to get into bed. He lowered himself onto the bed but then fell off the side. We struggled to get him up, and we succeeded. Then placing his bottom in the right spot so he could let himself down on the right spot on his pillow was another struggle. I braced myself at the foot of the bed so he could use my straight arm to pull himself up and into position. We finally achieved our goal and got him settled for the night.

My big concern is that he'll fall when he least expects it. Tonight he nearly fell in the bathroom because he got tangled up in his towel, and later in the bedroom he lost his balance putting on his slippers and tumbled, fortunately, onto the bed. His weakness is so great and his balance so poor that there's no way he can stop himself if he starts to fall.

Tomorrow I go for my yearly MRI. Since I have no symptoms, I'm sure the tumor hasn't grown, and I could put it off, but I feel I need to stay on schedule. Chuck's balance is so poor I can't leave him alone, so I'll ask Len Hapkins, Chuck's dear friend, to come. Len and Chuck are good friends, and Chuck feels very comfortable with him.

I still have my cellular phone, but when I'm in the MRI, I'll be out of contact, and that makes me very nervous. With Len, however, I feel reassured, and Chuck is OK about it.

AUGUST 8, 1994

The other shoe has dropped. Michelle says that her best guess has me in bed full-time within two weeks, and perhaps my death will occur in four weeks or so.

There is a recurring theme to our visitors' conversations. They talk about the influence Martha and I have had on them in the manner in which we face death. They ask how we managed to develop such strength, and they discuss with us their inability to face the issues surrounding their own deaths and those of their beloveds.

Martha and I refer frequently to that wintry night in January 1943, when we lay on the floor before a dancing fire. There I asked her to marry me. Then we prayed to God that He would give us mountains to climb *together*. We committed ourselves to each other, in a relationship that not only focused on each other but also focused our vision outward on something greater than us. Our determination to fulfill this mutual commitment continues even in these final days together.

It appears our commitment is being fulfilled in the influence we seem to be having on others as we face death and separation together. During these weeks and months when I prayed that the dying process would not be prolonged, I wondered why it was going so slowly. Now perhaps I am seeing the reason.

AUGUST 11, 1994

With his great weakness, I can no longer get Chuck from the bed to the bathroom. I don't want him to fall again, so I called hospice and they came right away and put in a Foley catheter.

Tomorrow the hospice nurse comes, and I'm going to ask for more help. I feel I need to have a stronger person bathe him, as I'm afraid of dropping him in the shower.

The love and caring from our friends is overwhelming. They are bringing dinner two or three times a week. How will I ever be able to thank them adequately?

AUGUST 13, 1994

How long can this go on? I have literally gone to pot with incredible speed. For the record:

• My left side is useless.
• I list to the left whether sitting or standing.
• It is impossible to get from sitting to standing, or vice versa, without help.
• I have a Foley catheter.
• I can neither bathe nor dress myself without help.
• Reading is difficult, both seeing the word and absorbing its meaning.
• Conversation is difficult, as words don't seem to flow with the facility of the past.

But, hallelujah, writing is still possible, so I can continue my journal. I feel hopeless and totally dependent, and I have never before experienced such feelings. I hope and pray for release.

AUGUST 15, 1994

Michelle just left and now says the end will come, in her judgment, in a matter of days. She was surprised herself, she said, having previously thought I would survive her maternity leave. Now, she says, no way. While she expects to be here in three or four days, we said our farewells just in case, and she shed a tear. A dear lady. I don't know how she can tell the end is coming.

Since I wrote the above, Terri and Jerry, the Village nurses, have come and gone. Admittedly I was sharper during their visit than I was during Michelle's, and no doubt I looked a lot better, but Terri and Jerry saw death in somewhat more protracted terms and seemed to say that two to four weeks was more probable.

While this is surely more than a turf matter, the Village nurse, who obviously sees herself as in charge, may well have a difference of opinion with the hospice nurse, who is in charge.

This clearly puts the patient in the dilemma of being caught between differences of opinion. Differences of opinion surrounding the probable date of my death take a special effort of understanding. I expressed to the Village nurses my discomfort with them and told them I didn't want them second-guessing Michelle, which, of course, they both denied, almost in unison.

AUGUST 17, 1994

Ten days ago, Chuck was walking with his cane; then he went to a walker; and now he's in a wheelchair. My heart aches as I see him try to use his left arm and hand and nothing happens. He's so wobbly and unsure that when he grabs hold of anything, he grips it securely.

Tom was here, and we had a precious day with him. At dinner, we were having soup and scones, one of Chuck's favorite meals, and it was really the first time the weakness in his hand and arm showed up significantly. He was trying to put some blueberry jam on the scone, and there was no way he could get his left hand to cooperate with his right, so as he daubed the jam on the scone, it ended up on his hand. He was very embarrassed, but he kept trying and said he'd get that scone in his mouth. He did, but with great difficulty. It's hard for me not to come to his rescue, but I let him do as much as he can. It's so important to him.

He fell Saturday evening as I was putting him on the toilet. I had taken him into the bathroom in his wheelchair, and as I was transferring him to the commode, he slipped into the tiny space between the two, and there was no way I could lift him back up. He sank to the floor until the nurses came to pick him up. For a little humor, he asked me to get the camera and take his picture for the record, which I did.

Going to church Sunday was impossible. It was a hard weekend, and I'm so sad!

AUGUST 19, 1994

"Chuck," asked my six-year-old grandson, Max, when he got on the phone from Tom's house, "are you going to die?"

"Yes, Max, I am," I replied.

"When?"

"Gosh, Max, I don't know. We don't know in advance."

He persisted. "What happens when you die?"

"Well, Max," I said, "everything stops working. You stop breathing, your heart stops, and your brain. It's like when your daddy turns the key to stop his car. Everything just stops working."

"Oh, dear," said Max.

AUGUST 20, 1994

Michelle says she gives Chuck two to four more weeks. That time frame seems impossible to me, yet when I see how helpless he is, I believe it.

I can be so strong at the time I'm told things like this, but as the words make their way from my head to my soul, I disintegrate in tears. When I look on the top of his dresser and see his keys, pocketknife, wallet, and change, and know they'll never be in his pockets again, the lump in my throat presses to be released in weeping. I ironed the trousers he last wore and hung them in his closet. Oh, how I wish he'd wear them again!

Karen came again, just at the right time, and helped us more than she'll ever realize. She pitched in and was constantly there when needed. Her strong support was everywhere, helping Chuck, in the kitchen, answering the phone, and sharing her love with both of us. When she left, I felt whole again.

Tom flew in today. He arrived about 11:00 a.m. and stayed until evening. He read "Thoughts on the Death of a Friend," a paper in which he had put down his feelings about his dad. It was wonderful for Chuck to hear the impact he has had on Tom, and I'm glad Tom read it to him. How fortunate Tom is to have had Chuck not only for a father, but also as a mentor and friend.

The time came for Tom to depart, and he said he thought this would be his final visit and farewell. We cried as we held each other and shared our love.

And then he was gone, leaving behind memories. Goodbye, Tom. I love you. I love you. I love you.

AUGUST 24, 1994

Shortly Doug's parents, Harv and Ruth Smith, will be here. What dear people they are to drive all the way from Akron for a ten-minute visit. How lucky we have been to have had such a wonderful and abiding relationship with the Smiths, ever since Karen and Doug became engaged. Not all families are so fortunate.

This is the moment Martha and I have long talked about, as we wondered whether I would be able to write my journal up to the bitter end. She has reassured me it would be possible, as she would transcribe from my notes, even as she sat at my bedside. Indeed that is what's happening at this very minute.

What a dear lady! What a true friend and caregiver! Even as I dictate, tears are flowing over our cheeks. Parting is so sad. My God, I don't want to leave her! This is the true pain, much harder than the physical pain of cancer itself.

WEDNESDAY, AUGUST 24, 1994

Chuck awakened me, saying his neck was hurting terribly, so I got up and rearranged his pillows. I crawled back into bed, and all of a sudden Chuck said, "Look, I can move my left leg."

I looked and saw that both legs were moving, and by the time I got to his side of the bed, he was shaking all over in a seizure. I called Karen; she came running from the den and stood by him while I called Riverside Hospice and the nurse from the clinic. When I returned to the bedside, all Chuck's limbs were flailing, his eyes were rolling, and his tongue was moving rapidly in his mouth. He begged us to hold his arms and legs down. Just as suddenly as it began, the seizure stopped, but we were all terrified and drained.

The hospice nurse drew some blood for tests, and Dr. Cindi came down from her office. She told us that among prostate cancer patients an embolism was frequently the cause of death. It's also common, she said, for a prostate cancer patient to produce more calcium than the body can process, and death follows rapidly, within forty-eight to seventy-two hours.

The blood tests showed no abundance of calcium, and an embolism was also ruled out, so it's probable that tumors are pushing on a critical part of the brain. He may never have another seizure or it may happen several more times. Dr. Cindi added Valium to his medications to calm him down and relax his muscles. She told us all to rest. We took her advice, Chuck because he was too exhausted to leave his bed, and Karen and I because we were too emotionally and physically spent to do anything else.

Tonight we all ate dinner together in Chuck's room. In spite of the day's stresses and his fatigue, he had quite an appetite. This puzzled the nurses at the Village, who felt that as long as his appetite was good, he had a long way to go.

Chuck was so frustrated by their remarks. He hates the thought that things will have to get worse before he can be delivered. Karen asked Dr. Cindi about it, and Dr. Cindi said the pain intervention had been so successful he might die without ever having lost his appetite. When Karen told Chuck, he was so relieved. "I'm glad I don't have to stop eating," he said, "just to prove to everyone how rotten I feel."

THURSDAY, AUGUST 25, 1994

To have Karen with me is to know peace. She is always at the right place at the right moment. One of her most important gifts to me is that she can position Chuck to make him more comfortable in bed. His paralysis makes it difficult for him to maneuver, and after the falls he and I have had, I know my strength isn't sufficient to move him very far.

But Karen and Chuck have perfected a sort of bear-hug style of movement. Chuck drapes his right arm around her shoulder, and she wraps him in a tender, yet strong embrace. On the count of three, they somehow work together, and she virtually lifts him whichever way he wants to go. At the beginning, Chuck worried he would hurt her back, and of course it's a constant challenge to Karen not to hurt his spine, since it's so very touchy from the cancer that has settled in the vertebrae.

I looked in a few times as Karen was working her magic, and I saw so much more than the physical act of positioning. She and Chuck look into each other's eyes; they hug and kiss. He says he feels secure in her arms. He says how grateful he is that she is with us again, as she always is at the crucial times. I hear the two of them reliving special moments—making ice cream, grilling chicken, enjoying father-daughter dinners. She tells him she loves him so much. He says, "I've never doubted that for a moment."

How do those who don't have a Karen or a Tom in their lives get through days like these? Thank you again, Lord.

FRIDAY, AUGUST 26, 1994

Last evening Chuck became very eager to see dear and special friends and to say goodbye. The idea came over him very quickly, and he was most adamant about it. He wanted to talk with Gary Garber, the music director at St. Mark's, and Michael Murray, the resident organist, and to tell them how much their friendship has meant to him. He wanted to do it immediately. Michael and Gary came straight-away from working in their garden.

After they left, and Karen and I were getting Chuck ready for sleep, he asked me to call other friends he wanted to see one final time. His list grew and grew. How would he have the strength? How would I? But it was so important to him, I could do nothing but make the calls. It was the beginning of an experience I will never fully understand but will hold in my heart until I die.

No one refused to come, even though I knew it would be very hard on many of them. At 8:00 this morning, a rivulet of friends began to arrive. It soon grew to a flood. Singles and couples came every half hour, their visits sometimes overlapping, until 5:30 this evening, when more than forty people had come and gone. The living room was full all day, and it wasn't quiet. Visitors conversed with one another and with me, and as one emerged from our room, I would lead the next group to Chuck's bedside.

It was quieter there, and during the hours Chuck made his farewells, the room began to take on a strong, palpable energy, a shimmering pulsation. It was as if all the memories Chuck shared with these special visitors were colliding like atoms, creating a fusion of souls. Slowly, slowly his room became a sanctified space. I can't really explain it except to say that the love and remembrance and laughter and tears gathered around Chuck somehow called the Holy Spirit into that place. The Presence was unmistakable and over-whelming. And instead of becoming depleted, Chuck grew stronger and more vibrant with each hour. By dinnertime, when the last guest departed, he looked at me, his face suffused with joy and said, "What a glorious day!"

It gave me such deep satisfaction to see him with his friends as they recalled their days together and said good-bye. Yes, it was heart-breaking for me to witness these farewells. Yes, I was emotionally spent when the day was over, but it was a sacred time, an occasion of such an overflowing abundance of God's grace, I could only be grate-ful to be part of it.

Tom arrives tomorrow, and Chuck promises to do his best to die when we are all together. I know he wants to move on, but when he says things like this, he shatters the glass jar in which I've enclosed myself. It's safe in the jar. I can see and I can hear and I can talk and I can function. I just can't feel. When Chuck's honesty fractures the glass, the shards and splinters pierce my heart. My soul bleeds. I do not think I can bear the pain.

Saturday, August 27, 1994

Chuck didn't die today. Instead, as he talked with Tom, he savored a long, cool Scotch. I guess the combination of morphine and liquor really isn't dangerous anymore, so they just enjoyed it.

SUNDAY, AUGUST 28, 1994

Today began with Holy Communion, which Michael and Barbara brought to us. It was a lovely service with many tears, and afterward the Jupins stayed for a few minutes just to converse and to be what help they could be to Chuck and me. Admittedly, though, there's really nothing anyone can do.

Chuck so wants to be done with the dying! After Michael and Barbara left, he asked me to read the meditations for those near death and struggling to let go. As I read, he fell into such a deep sleep Karen and I were sure he would just slip away. We were riveted on him, unable to leave the bedside. There was no sound. We sat together for three hours, Chuck clasping my hand. Karen occasionally rested her head in his lap, but then, worried she might physically be holding him back from his departure, she moved away to give him a sense of freedom, to literally let him go.

From this blessed stillness, Chuck suddenly woke. "Am I dying?" he said.

"I've never told you a lie, and I'm not starting now," I said. "Yes, you are dying."

He looked momentarily confused and said, "I had the most fantastic dream, all night long. Michael was here, and Barbara. She was wearing a red dress. . . ." Karen and I told him that everything he was describing really had happened. We thought it would reassure him to know he was still with us and it all wasn't a dream.

He wasn't reassured. "Everything I dreamed was real?" he asked. He began to weep, from somewhere deep inside. "Then this really is happening. I really am dying. I dreamed about this day, and I dreamed I was dying, and I didn't want to die, and I didn't want to leave you. That's why I asked. I wanted you to tell me I wasn't."

My heart spun in my chest. For the first time in our married life, I should have lied to him. At the time he was most vulnerable and I most wanted to ease his pain, my truth-telling brought him nothing but anguish. Through my own tears, I told him how sorry I was to have hurt him so deeply. And with unspeakable kindness, he forgave me and said it was important for me to continue speaking the truth.

Karen believes Chuck really was dying, but was unable to go forward. She thinks that in our concern for releasing him, we have forgotten to help him release us. All I know is that Chuck is like a puppy on a chain, boundlessly eager to explore life beyond the far edge of his yard. But whenever he steps a foot beyond those confines, his tether relentlessly pulls him back into the place he knows. I am the tether, and I want to let him slip his collar and go on adventuring, but how can I? How can I wish for his death? How can I not?

MONDAY, AUGUST 29, 1994

After the peace and terror of Sunday afternoon, Chuck rallied in the evening. He ate a huge dinner and even joked that his would be the best-stuffed corpse the funeral directors had ever seen.

And today even more people came to say good-bye. I arranged it so Melody would be his last visitor. She stayed for happy hour, but when she got up to leave, Chuck said, "Mel, help me die."

She took both his hands in hers. "Chuck," she answered, her voice tender, "God gave you an enormous zest for this life. You can't turn it off easily. But you know when God gave you this life, He also promised you another one that's eternal. He will keep His promise. When it is time, your heart, which knows the way, will take you there."

TUESDAY, AUGUST 30, 1994

When Chuck woke this morning, he was very subdued and asked me to read the meditations again. Then Karen read the liturgy Michael had left on Sunday. Patrice came, and Chuck asked for her help in letting go. As Patrice sat by his bedside and spoke of horizons, Chuck recalled memories of New England and fell into a quiet sleep. Michelle looked in on him and suggested we keep the world out today—to give him space and time. Terri and Jerry, the Village nurses, came over, looked from afar, and said the end was very near. And at 5:15, Chuck waved to me and asked for dinner! He surely has one foot in this world and one in the next.

TUESDAY, AUGUST 30, 1994

The screaming clock says 6:09 p.m. I just awakened from a "long summer's nap." Martha has her trusty laptop on her lap as she sits on the edge of her bed and I eat my breakfast from my bed tray—oatmeal smothered in blueberries and blueberry muffins smothered in peanut butter. Karen is to my left, dutifully wiping the dribbles from my chin. Some wise person said, "It's certainly hard to do good." He might well have said, "It's equally hard to die."

This is Tuesday evening, and I've been trying to die since Sunday. It never occurred to me that death would come this hard; it simply eludes me. What can I say? Everyone who has visited me today has had ideas, and I've tried them all. Some say just to relax and let it happen, while others say, "Let it come from your peace." I'm sure it's good advice, but I have a theory of my own, which is simply that one dies in the same manner in which he has lived. For me, that means "in charge." In life, I have lived in charge of everything around me, and in death I am attempting to die in charge of the process—the antithesis of so much of the above advice.

So now the screaming clock says 6:29 p.m., my oatmeal bowl is empty, the delicious blueberry muffin is gone. I have taken my Elavil, under duress, and am sipping on my coffee. I hope I die tonight. If I don't, I will awaken in the morning angry at myself, with my diapers loaded, and there's no pleasure in that thought!

Martha is getting restless as she leans against a pile of pillows, her laptop poised as I dictate. Karen will return to Boston this week and we'll sure miss her, although she just advised me, "I'm not going anywhere." I sure hope I do—the sooner, the better. So this marks the end of my journal. It has been a pleasure to write.

Farewell, goodbye, and God bless.

WEDNESDAY, AUGUST 31, 1994

Colby telephoned. "It's a good thing you called, ole buddy," Chuck said, "because I'm about ready to check out." When Karen spoke with Colby, however, he told her he had felt for weeks that Chuck would die on a Tuesday. Karen told him there was no way her dad could go on that long, but Colby's feelings were not to be denied. He told his mother just to watch and wait.

THURSDAY, SEPTEMBER 1, 1994

This morning Chuck asked me if it was September first. For some reason, for the last two or three days he has thought it was September and was disappointed when I told him it was still August. When I said it was September, he seemed relieved. I don't know why, and I guess I never will.

He has slept most of the day and didn't rouse when I kissed him or stroked his face. Close to 7:30 p.m., he woke agitated. "It's time I got up, got out of here. I've been lying around here long enough! How long has it been? . . . I have to get up. . . . I'm supposed to meet someone for breakfast. . . . Who am I supposed to meet? I have to get up.

I don't want to be late. . . . Help me get to the car." He was determined to get out of bed. Karen and I explained to him that he was partially paralyzed and that we couldn't get him into the car. "But I'm expected," he said. Karen finally got his datebook and showed him there was no breakfast meeting scheduled.

I wonder if in our earthbound reality, we once again held him back from his most important appointment. Who was waiting? Are they ready for him now?

FRIDAY–SUNDAY, SEPTEMBER 2–4, 1994

I have been sleeping with my head at the foot of my twin bed pulled snugly next to his hospital bed. This way we can hold hands all night, and I can see his face when I open my eyes. I awaken several times, like a new mother listening to every breath of her baby.

Friday, Chuck startled in his sleep. "I hurt, I hurt," he said, his eyes wide with pain and helplessness. He could no longer swallow his medication. But I'm not helpless, and I wouldn't allow him pain. I prayed for help and telephoned Arthur, who answered my call and my prayer.

He brought the pain override medicine to the house himself and had a port put into Chuck's arm so that he could receive his medication without swallowing. Arthur also wrote a prescription for an anti-seizure medication to be injected every eight hours. Chuck's will truly be the death he wanted, the good death.

Karen and I continue to talk to him and to hold his hands. I snuggle myself into his warm neck. He's aware of our presence, and we have a great need to be with him. Our apartment is like a warm, soft blanket, and both Karen and I are content to stay close. Chuck's room is still filled with an ineffable aura. There is not that first hint of fear in it.

Margo came from church with communion for us. Chuck never roused for communion but seemed, mysteriously, to be very much in tune with what was going on. His lips moved when we said the Lord's Prayer; at the places in the service where he would normally cross himself, he would make the attempt. At those times I took his right hand and helped him do it. It seemed to give him peace.

Tonight will be the first time I've needed a night nurse, but according to the schedule Karen and I have set up for Chuck's medications, there is something to do every two hours. With that kind of timetable, there will be no way for Karen and me to get any sleep, and we must sleep. As I put one foot in front of the other, I don't feel tired, but I know the fatigue is lurking like a lion in the tall grass. Once I let down my guard, it will eat me alive.

This will be the first night I haven't slept in Chuck's room with my bed next to his. Tonight I will sleep in the den with Karen. I wonder if I can sleep without holding his hand.

MONDAY, SEPTEMBER 5, 1994

Chuck is in a coma now. He doesn't react to any of our stroking or talking, but that doesn't keep Karen and me from continuing to do so.

As I sit by his bed, I wonder how I can ever be whole again. Our mutual gaze has been turned outward so long, it has become one perspective. Our hands have been clasped so long, they've become one hand. Our souls have danced together so long, they've become one spirit. When he is gone, I will be half-blind and unable to feel the music of the dance.

My faith is unwavering. I know Chuck will not be alone on his journey, and I also have the Risen Lord as my companion. But sure as I am of the truth of this, right now all these words feel like pious platitudes. It is nearly over, and I am numb.

TUESDAY, SEPTEMBER 6, 1994

At midnight, as I open the door for the nurse, Karen comes and says there is a change in Chuck's breathing. The three of us hurry to the bedroom. His breathing is more shallow, more rapid, and accompanied by small gasps for breath. Karen is on one side of the bed, I on the other; the nurse is sitting at the foot of the bed. Karen and I hold his hands, watching and listening, not knowing quite what to expect. Suddenly, quietly, the nurse says, "Get ready, here we go," and with that Chuck's breathing slows down to a deep sigh—and silence.

Karen and I bury our heads on his body and dissolve into sobs. After more than a minute, Chuck takes a huge breath and starts to breathe again, slowly. We sit up quickly, look at one another, and immediately experience the same thought—that Chuck is trying once more to get back into his body, to spare us pain. It hurts him to see us crying. Simultaneously, we tell him we are sad, but that it's all right for him to die.

In a moment, he is quiet, and he is gone—on a Tuesday, as Colby said.

I telephone Tom to find he wakened at the time of Chuck's death. My call does not surprise him.

The next three hours pass in a haze. Karen and I help move in and out of the room, reflecting, feeling, sensing Chuck's presence. We help the hospice nurse clear away all evidence of medication and medical equipment. Chuck's body is still in the bed. But as time passes, it becomes unquestionably clear that he has shed his wounded vessel. His soul and spirit have been taken to their new home. The undertaker comes. He asks me if I want to step into another room while he removes the body from the apartment. Of course not. I will witness all the journey.

It is finally over. The path Chuck and I have been walking these eight years, with our hands clasped, has come to its fork, and our hands have slipped slowly apart until our fingers are no longer touching. But the golden thread that binds our hearts together is unbreakable.

Thanks be to God.

4

Martha's Path

(Epilogue)

The first year after Chuck's death is past, and I survived it! I expected to survive it, but there were times when all I could do was take one day at a time and put one foot in front of the other. As I did that, the days turned into weeks and the weeks to months. The months ended in a year, and here I am. There's no doubt I'm a stronger person than I was at this time last year. I was a wounded chick, and when I looked into the future, I saw nothing.

There are many things I've learned these past twelve months, and there have been times I've been consumed with grief, but I have never lost my zest for life, and I wanted to remain as open as possible to what experiences might take place.

In the eight years of Chuck's struggle, the most outstanding thing I learned was to look a problem straight in the face and deal with it. The cancer wouldn't go away, but looking right at it enabled me to live without burdening my mind by trying to avoid reality. I also learned to accept each new problem as it came along; acceptance brings peace with it.

As I applied these tools to my current problems, I found that when I faced my aloneness and accepted the fact that Chuck had died (although I had to redo this acceptance several times), I could find peace. With that peace, I could be aware of life around me and aware of opportunities to learn and grow.

Pursuing my spiritual growth has been a wonderful experience. I have not been alone; I have been guided and sustained by God and Jesus Christ through the Holy Spirit. I have no way of proving this except by what I feel. I have been given strength and courage, and I'm grateful!

Tom and Karen have been so supportive and loving, as have all the family, and our friends have been superb with their love and caring.

This doesn't mean there haven't been times of deep grief. Far from it! What it does mean is that when those periods hit, I gave myself permission to grieve and cry. Then I would pick myself up and know I could go on. Each time I was stronger.

Another tool that aided me was talk. Chuck and I always said, "Time, talk, and tears will heal," and they always have. I missed my buddy with whom I could talk in depth, so to whom was I going to talk? I talked with my computer and have kept a journal for this past year. I also found I could continue to be open with Tom and Karen. At first, I didn't want to burden them with my feelings of hurt, but they were hurting too, so we shared, and it made us all feel better.

My dear friend Margo always has an open ear and arms. Michael, my rector, has been wonderful in listening and caring. This past month has been hard for me, and I couldn't understand why I felt as though I were back at square one. Michael helped me see that as this year has progressed, I have permitted myself to experience more and more feelings. In the beginning, my mind protected me by not allowing me to feel as deeply as I do now. I understood what he was saying, and it felt right.

A trip to China was a big step in my development, because it was then I realized I could cope on my own, even in going to a foreign country. I have to admit I feel it was a great accomplishment.

I've been fortunate to be involved with people from Ohio State University Medical Center, who have asked me to help them. Dr. Arthur H. asked if he could interview me on tape about Chuck's pain management and how it helped his quality of life. This tape was viewed by other physicians throughout the state. Another man who teaches first- and third-year medical students about death and dying saw the tape. He, in turn, called me and asked if I would be willing to talk to medical students about the doctor-patient relationship. I am willing to talk to anyone about Chuck's cancer and our coping if I can be helpful to others.

The journals Chuck and I kept are being edited, and that is exciting, because we always hoped they would be useful. The prospect that they may help others gives me joy and peace. Telling others about our journey is very healing for me, but that's not why I do it. I do it to assist others. I'm grateful for the by-product, however.

Today I am aware that I want not only to live each day, but also to do so in depth. It's important that I experience each day. I want to taste each day. I want to feel each day. I'm not afraid to feel, as the wound from Chuck's death is not as open as it used to be. It's still there, but the scab is firmer, and it takes a little more to make it bleed. I feel that I've been led by God. I've asked God what's next and to help me be aware of it.

To live each day fully and to be aware of it is a precious gift.

Thoughts On
The Death of a Friend

Thomas E. Wheeler

C HUCK WHEELER was a man with a fascination for words.

Who else would have kept a dictionary under the front seat of the car to look up the meaning of a word he had just heard? Who else would proudly correct menus which had misspelled *vichys-soise?* Chuck Wheeler was a man who loved what words could do.

He was a salesman extraordinary who lived on his ability to couple analysis with the right words to stimulate a sale.

He was a speaker before audiences large and small who delighted in the ability of his words to motivate.

He was a writer who left for us all not only a written history of one man's journey, but also a treatise entitled "A Stray Dog" about his experience with the black dog of cancer nipping at his heels.

There is no better way to celebrate Chuck Wheeler than in his own words.

The expression of Dad's which leaps immediately to mind might not seem appropriate for this occasion because, in the raw, it is slightly off color. This version is cleaned up a bit. Dad use to say that "making love isn't a halfway thing."

Living life wasn't a halfway thing for Dad. He use to drive Karen and me crazy, as kids, when he'd come to awaken us in the morning, shouting at the top of his lungs, "Arise! Another day charged with opportunity!"

That's what life was for Dad—a series of opportunities which you met head on—with your full resources.

Even at the end of his life Dad practiced this indefatigable drive for life. As he grew weaker and weaker he became paralyzed, first on his left side. We were having dinner one Saturday night shortly after this paralysis began. He propped his barely-functioning left hand on the dinner table around one on Mom's great scones. He was bound and determined to make that hand cooperate as he tried to spread blueberry jelly on the scone, using the knife in his good right hand. Mom and I sat there watching as, with tears in his eyes, he repeatedly said, "I can do it," and tried to make his left hand work through sheer force of will.

I had had occasion over the years to test that will once or twice; I was betting on him. But, alas, the body was weaker than the will was strong.

His determination to continue to attack life and its challenges, even as life deserted him, is engraved in us all.

My favorite word—that only he could use—was the name Elmer, his nickname for me. To be a good salesman is a gift of God, and it turns out that the self-proclaimed "World's Greatest Salesman" was a man named Elmer Wheeler. He was no relation, but it was Elmer Wheeler who coined "Sell the sizzle, not the steak." When it turned out that young Tom had been passed the gene of salesmanship, I suddenly became "Elmer" Wheeler. It was the compliment that one salesman pays to another. Dad practiced a salesmanship with several special components.

Recently I was asked by a newspaper to name my greatest inspiration. The reply: "My father, Chuck Wheeler, who prized salesmanship, integrity, and commitment to others."

Dad used his God-given gift to provide for his family and for the benefit of others. I remember many the night, sitting at the dinner table with Dad recounting something he had done during the day in one of his many civic activities. He'd get frustrated that things weren't going as fast as they should or in the direction he had been advocating; he'd shake his head and observe, "God, it's hard to do good."

Dad was a man who didn't have a sales pitch, he had a philosophy. Whether he was selling you life insurance or the United Way, he was selling a belief. And he practiced his beliefs.

He practiced the fiscal discipline and planning that he sold to his clients. It became a mantra as we grew up (usually heard during the last week of the month) that we were "broke, but in good financial shape."

I know he was proud that, as a result of practicing the philosophy he sold for a living, one of the things that he and Mom *didn't* have to worry about during the trials of the last several years was how they would provide for not only the medical care, but also Mom's future.

And, while we're talking about money and the legacy of a man who spent his life counseling others about their assets, there's Chuck Wheeler's Indisputable Law of Capital: "There are only three things you can do with money—you can spend it, you can save it, and you can give it away." The first one is easy; the second one (actually first in his pantheon) much harder; the third an act of witness.

Rights and responsibilities, that's what it all boiled down to. "I have the right to swing my fist wherever I want," he would say, "up to the point where your nose begins." Dad was a man who stood for the rights of individuals—I think that was what made him a Democrat—and who just as fervently believed that those rights brought with them responsibilities.

The abiding preeminence in Dad's life is expressed in the oft-repeated words, "Your Mom is a hell of a woman!" The relationship between Chuck and Martha Wheeler defined love, an overwhelming love—a love of shared experiences, belief and commitment which, as they explored together the terminal years, appeared to grow even richer.

Finally, for me, the *most* special word of Dad's was the word *friend*. We had a friendship surpassing the relationship of a father and son. On my fifteenth birthday he took me aside and told me that I was now old enough to begin living my own life and that he would try, henceforth, to always be a father, but also to make a new commitment, to treat me with the respect of a friend. I, of course, had no idea at the time what he was talking about.

During the ensuing thirty-three years I have experienced, as a father myself, the challenge of the goal he set for himself.

A friend always stands in support.

A friend revels in your victories and wails at your defeats.

A father brings life, lessons, and examples. A friend gives you the space to practice, even imperfectly, what you've learned.

A friend exults in you becoming your own person.

He left us a legacy, anchored in his words. He practiced the philosophy behind those words, right up to the end.

We all will miss him.

His words survive.

GLOSSARY

Androgen deprivation Treatment of prostate cancer by depriving the prostate of the male hormone androgen.

Biopsy The removal of a small piece of tissue for microscopic examination to establish or confirm a diagnosis.

Bone scan A radiographic technique that helps visualize abnormal activity. A radioactive substance is intravenously injected and concentrates in the bone. It is then visualized using a scanning device.

Breaking down The reopening of a wound that has previously healed, oftentimes because of an infection or improperly healed tissues. In particular, it may occur with tissues that have been treated with radiation therapy.

Chemotherapy The use of chemicals for symptomatic relief of cancer. The most commonly used chemicals are Veldan and Emsyt, which can be used on their own or together. A more potent agent is Suramin, but it is used only in younger patients because of concerns for its side effects, which are sometimes worse than the pain Suramin is meant to relieve.

Colostomy Surgical creation of an artificial anus in the abdominal wall by cutting the colon and bringing it out to the surface

---

This glossary was compiled with the generous assistance of pain specialist Costantino Benedetti, M.D., and urologist John Burgers, M.D., both of Columbus, Ohio.

of the abdomen. It is performed for cancer of the colon, benign tumors obstructing the intestine, and severe abdominal wounds.

Crohn's disease A chronic inflammatory bowel disease of unknown origin. It usually affects the ileum, the colon, or both.

CT scan A computerized x-ray technique that produces hundreds of pictures taken from all angles, from which a three-dimensional view of the body can be created. In prostate cancer this procedure is not particularly useful because the cancer doesn't show up until it's quite advanced.

Cystoscopy The direct visualization of the urinary tract by means of a cystoscope inserted in the urethra. Cystoscopy is also used for obtaining biopsies of tumors or other growths and for the removal of polyps.

Dilaudid A pain medication similar to morphine.

Dulcolax A medication for the treatment of constipation.

Elavil An antidepressant medication which is also helpful in treating some types of pain and improving sleep patterns.

Embolism An abnormal circulatory condition in which a blood clot, an air bubble, fatty material, or any other large particle travels through the bloodstream and becomes lodged in a blood vessel.

Epidural catheter A small hollow tube the size of a fishing line inserted in the space close to the spinal cord (the epidural space) and used to deliver medication for pain control (oftentimes morphine and/or a local anesthetic).

Escape A layman's term sometimes used by doctors to describe *metastasis*, as in "the cancer has escaped."

Fluoroscope A device used for the immediate projection of a continuous x-ray image on a fluorescent screen for visual examination.

Flutamide A medication used to block the effect of the male hormone.

Foley Catheter A type of hollow rubber tube inserted in the urinary bladder for urine drainage.

Gleason Scale A two-stage grading system that measures the aggressiveness of cancer cells by comparing them with normal cells under a microscope. In the first stage, cells taken from the largest tissue area affected by the cancer are compared with normal cells and then graded from 1 (most like normal) to 5 (most cancerous). In the second stage, the same comparison is made using cells taken from the second-largest area affected by the cancer, again graded on a 1-to-5 scale. The two results are added together to produce an overall Gleason score of the disease, ranging from 2 (most normal) to 10 (most abnormal).

Hormone treatment Although the female hormone estrogen is no longer used to treat prostate cancer, because of the high risk of heart attack in patients who receive it, other hormones are still used frequently, in conjunction with other methods like orchiectomy.

IVP (intravenous pyelography) The intravenous injection of a substance used to visualize the kidneys and the urinary tract using x-ray.

Low-grade (cancer cells) Beginning stages of cancer.

Metastasis The process by which tumor cells spread to distant parts of the body. Metastatic cancer is a cancer that has spread from its origin to a distant site.

MRI (magnetic resonance imaging) A technique that uses magnetic fields instead of x-rays to visualize parts of the body.

MS Contin A controlled-release, or sustained-release, morphine pill, which lasts eight to twelve hours and is used to treat long-lasting, intense pain.

NCI National Cancer Institute.

Orchiectomy Removal of a testicle to decrease male hormone production.

Palliation The branch of medicine that deals with the treatment of pain and symptoms associated with any disease for which a cure is not likely.

Penile implant (prosthesis) A device that can be surgically implanted in the penis of males who cannot obtain an erection. There are many different types of implants, all made from silicone and filled with saline. Of the three most common types, the first is a three-piece model with a pump in the scrotum, a reservoir in the abodmen, and the silicone device implanted inside a cavity in the penis; the second is a two-piece model, similar to the three-piece, but without an implant in the abdomen; the third is malleable and implanted in the penis only.

Percocet A combination of pain medications, one similar to morphine, the other a generic form of Tylenol.

Prostate A male gland surrounding the neck of the bladder and the urethra and producing a substance that liquefies coagulated semen.

Prostatectomy Surgical removal of the prostate gland.

PSA (prostate-specific antigen) A protein made by the prostate and secreted into the blood stream. Although its purpose is unknown, it is believed to liquefy semen. It may increase in patients with prostate cancer or other abnormal conditions of the prostate.

Radiation (therapy) A form of cancer treatment using radioactive substances.

Radiation enteritis Inflammation of the intestine due to radiation therapy.

Radiation oncologist A physician who specializes in the treatment of cancer using radiation therapy.

Remission A stage in which the cancer is not actively progressing.

Scopolamine Medication used for nausea.

Stages A, B, C, and D Progressive stages of cancer. Stage A is cancer found incidentally, by accident. In Stage B of prostate cancer a nodule is found contained within the prostate capsule. Stage C means the cancer extends outside the prostate capsule but not outside the local area of the prostate. Stage D means that the cancer has escaped into the bloodstream (metastasized) and can be found elsewhere in the body.

Steroids A cortisone-like medication sometimes used for pain control.

Subarachnoid A space around the spinal cord filled with cerebral spinal fluid.

TIA (transient ischemic attack) A result of severe decrease in blood flow. If the low blood flow is to the brain it may cause fainting spells or severe dizziness.

Toradol A medication similar to aspirin.

Trilisate A medication similar to aspirin that may cause less gastric irritation.

Voltaren A medication similar to aspirin.

White Count The number of white blood cells in the blood stream. White cells are responsible for the body's immune response.

INDEX